Interactive Monte Carlo Experimentation

in Econometrics using

PcNaive 2

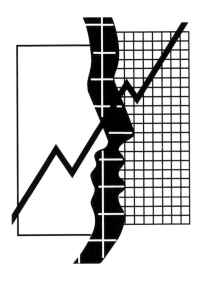

Interactive Monte Carlo Experimentation
in Econometrics using

PcNaive 2

Jurgen A. Doornik

David F. Hendry

Timberlake Consultants Ltd

A Leading Distributor of Statistical and Econometrics Software

PcNaive 2

British Library Cataloguing-in-Publication Data
A catalogue record for this book is available from the British Library

Published by Timberlake Consultants Press a Division of Timberlake Consultants Ltd.
Printed in the UK by Allstar Services, Harrow

Cover designed in the UK by CCA Design and Communications Ltd., London

ISBN 0-9533394-8-3

Timberlake Consultants Ltd
Unit B3, Broomsleigh Business Park, Worsley Bridge Road,
London SE26 5BN, United Kingdom
Tel: + 44 (0)20 8697 3377 Fax: + 44 (0)20 8697 3388
email: info@timberlake.co.uk   Website: http://www.timberlake.co.uk

Contents

IV Monte Carlo Theory   125

Figures

Example Programs

Preface

PcNaive is the latest in a long line of descendants of the original NAIVE program (see Hendry and Srba, 1980). Version 2 builds on version 1, but is essentially a completely new program both in structure and function. As well as being fully adapted for Windows, and adding many powerful features, PcNaive 2 now allows simulation investigations of complete systems of equations. Moreover, it outputs Ox code, which is then run by OxRun with the results sent to GiveWin, rather than directly computing the required statistics as in version 1. In addition, the documentation has been improved and expanded (despite first appearances to the contrary!).

The original mainframe ancestor was written in Fortran, and earlier PC versions in a mixture of Fortran with some C and Assembly. Version 2 is a complete rewrite in C++. Sections of code in earlier versions were contributed by Neil Ericsson, Robin Harrison, Giuseppe Mazzarino, Adrian Neale, Denis Sargan, Frank Srba and Juri Sylvestrowicz – their important contributions are gratefully acknowledged.

Over its life, many scholars, researchers and generations of students have contributed to the development of PcNaive by providing comments and testing out β-versions. We are grateful to them all for their help and encouragement. In particular, we wish to thank Julia Campos, Mike Clements, Neil Ericsson, Tony Hall, Grayham Mizon, Adrian Neale, Frank Srba, and Timo Teräsvirta. We are also grateful to the Oxford Department of Economics, especially to Gillian Coates, for help with earlier versions. And we wish to thank Maureen Baker and Nuffield College for their support over the years of development. Users of PcNaive have also made helpful suggestions for improving and extending its repertoire, and while version 2 will undoubtedly not yet satisfy all of their wishes, we remain grateful for their comments, and hope that they and others will continue to write with good ideas (and *report any bugs*!).

The documentation for NAIVE has evolved considerably since its inception. We are indebted to Robin Harrison and Frank Srba for their help in preparing the first (mainframe) version of a manual. Adrian Neale and Neil Ericsson were co-authors of the first PC version of the manual, and as we have borrowed heavily from their work in preparing this revised manual, we are very grateful for their important contributions.

The research and development of PcNaive has been financed in part by the Economic and Social Research Council under a series of grants extending over many years, from the first PC-version (HR8789), through B00220012, R231184 and R000234954 to R000237500. We are very grateful for their continuing support.

MikTeX in combination with dvips and GhostView eased the development of the documentation for version 2 in LaTeX. The editing was almost entirely undertaken using OxEdit, which allowed flexible incorporation of PcNaive output and LaTeX compilation, and HyperSnap-DX which enabled the screen captures (with bmp2eps for conversion to PostScript).

Both authors owe a considerable debt to their families for the long hours they spent on this project: their support and encouragement were essential, even though they could only benefit indirectly from the end product. In this respect DFH would like to particularly thank Evelyn and Vivien, and JAD is similarly indebted to Kate. We hope the benefits derived by others compensate.

We wish you enjoyable and productive use of
PcNaive for Windows

Part I

PcNaive Prologue

Chapter 1

Introduction to PcNaive

1.1 General information

PcNaive is an interactive menu-driven program for Monte Carlo study of econometric methods. Version 2 for GiveWin 2, to which this documentation refers, runs on Intel-compatible machines operating under Windows 2000 (as well as Windows 95/98/ME/NT).

PcNaive is designed for simulating on artificial data the range of estimators, tests, and modelling methods provided in **PcGive** (Hendry and Doornik, 2001, Doornik and Hendry, 2001b). Such experiments allow the finite-sample properties of these econometric methods to be evaluated in relevant settings. PcNaive formulates experiments by writing **Ox** code which is then executed by **OxRun** (see Doornik, 2001), therefore PcNaive requires the Professional version of Ox (version 3.0 or newer) . Particular features of the program are its ease for designing complicated Monte Carlo experiments, and its focus on recursive methods, supported by powerful graphics through GiveWin. Detailed tutorials in Chapters 4–8 teach Monte Carlo simulation by walking the user through the program in organized steps. This is supported by clear explanations of Monte Carlo methods in Chapter 14. The material spans the level from introductory to frontier research, with an emphatic orientation to practical modelling and evaluating the operational characteristics of inference procedures. The context-sensitive help system supports this approach by offering help on both the program and simulation.

This chapter discusses the special features of PcNaive, describes how to use the documentation, provides background information on interactive operation, help, results storage, and filenames, then outlines the basics of using the program (point-and-click with a mouse).

1.2 The special features of PcNaive

(1) PcNaive *is extremely easy to use*. It provides an interactive and menu-driven approach to Monte Carlo experimentation: screen menus offer the available op-

tions and 'live' screen editors make experimental design simple. In particular, although PcNaive operates via Ox, the command language of Ox does not have to be learned prior to efficient use.

(2) PcNaive is *specifically designed for Monte Carlo studies of time-series*. It flexibly creates experiments involving linear stochastic dynamic systems. Experimental designs are stored for later execution (so can be prepared in advance), revision (easily accomplished in the classroom), or extension.

(3) Estimated systems need not coincide with any relationships in the generating mechanism, so a *vast range of correct and mis-specified models* can be investigated, helping to bring theoretical econometric formulae to life.

(4) PcNaive offers the ability to study both *stationary and non-stationary* data processes by simulation; for stationary processes, finite-sample outcomes can be matched with numerical values of asymptotic results.

(5) PcNaive uses **Ox** for its numerical and graphical *algorithms*, so are fast, efficient and accurate and have been carefully tested (see e.g., Doornik, 1995, and Doornik, 2001).

(6) PcNaive uses the random number generator of L'Ecuyer (1997), which is well tested and has an extremely large period before it starts to repeat itself. This is a linear shift register (or Tausworthe) generator with period of approximately 2^{113}.

(7) The *user friendliness and screen presentations* are of the high quality that PC-users expect. When using **GiveWin** for output, all of its superb interactive graphics facilities are available.

(8) PcNaive allows pseudo-recursive estimation, thereby providing results on estimation and inference as functions of the sample size T. The output includes *live automatic graphing* of coefficient estimates, with both their Monte Carlo and econometric confidence intervals, as well as test properties: the rejection frequencies of parameter-constancy statistics are also calculated. Chapter 14 describes the underlying Monte Carlo methods. The simulation proceeds seriatim by any horizon (i.e., 1-step, n-step, or variable at different values of the sample size), and results are updated on screen in real time as the sample size changes.

(9) *Histograms and non-parametrically estimated data densities* describe between-replications distributional shapes: again, updated live on screen in real time.

(10) PcNaive in combination with Ox and GiveWin has a *high level of error protection* covering keyboard and file input, disk output, numerical calculations, graphics, and menu choices. This makes the program suitable for live teaching in

the classroom. However, protection against accidental input of nonsensical parameters is difficult in a Monte Carlo environment, due to the inherent nature of simulation experiments.

1.3 An overview of PcNaive

PcNaive is designed for analyzing estimators of dynamic econometric models, as implemented, for example, in the computer program PcGive (see Hendry and Doornik, 2001; PcGive is the companion econometric modelling program).

Simulation experiments are designed interactively, based on a dialog-driven approach, and can be simulated immediately or later, and analyzed at once or at leisure. PcNaive is essentially an *Ox Wizard*: based on user-supplied settings for the experiment, the program will write an Ox computer program. This Ox program is then run, with text and graphics output appearing in **GiveWin**.

We now describe the main features of PcNaive under five sub-headings each of which lists a desirable feature of a simulation package then describes how it is implemented in PcNaive.

- First, **a suitably-general artificial data generation process** must be incorporated into any Monte Carlo package, covering a wide range of dynamic processes, density functions, and other data features of relevance to empirical econometrics. Consequently, the baseline DGP in PcNaive is a multi-equation, stochastic, dynamic, linear, simultaneous system, allowing between- and within-equation contemporaneous and lagged feedbacks; constants; trends; unit roots, where sets of variables may or may not be cointegrated; structural breaks in conditional or marginal processes; scalar or vector autoregressive-moving average errors; autoregressive conditional heteroscedasticity; measurement errors; and many different forms of error (or data) distributions. Chapter 2 discusses this aspect of PcNaive, summarizing the baseline system.

- Secondly, it must be **easy, rapid, and reliable to change** the DGP, the estimators and tests under study, the model specification, or the experimental design, especially in a classroom setting. Thus, PcNaive provides an interactive menu-driven screen editor system to create and modify any desired aspects of an existing Monte Carlo experiment. A sequence of menus is offered, such that the prevailing values of the design parameters are shown on screen, and are altered by entering the new information directly into a relevant 'box'. The tutorials describe the input screen editors.

- Thirdly, **a wide range of model formulations and statistics of interest** must be open to study, in order to investigate the consequences of mis-specifications, changes in data properties, and alternative estimators and tests. In PcNaive, an estimated equation or system need not correspond to any equation in the DGP; there can be untreated residual autocorrelation or ARCH effects; exogeneity assumptions in a model may or may not be valid in the DGP; and a range of data transformations can be undertaken prior to equation estimation, including superimposing measurement errors between the generated data and that used in estimation. Structural breaks can be induced in either the conditional model of interest or in a marginal process. The asymptotic outcomes for parameter estimates are the subject of Chapter 16. Chapter III provides a discussion of some applications of PcNaive in teaching econometrics.

This book aims to facilitate learning how to use PcNaive productively. Part II provides step by step tutorials on designing and simulating experiments. Using GiveWin, the latest information on coefficient distributions and constancy tests is updated on-screen as replications proceed. Chapters 4–8 provide illustrative experiments. The population coefficients for many model specifications are automatically evaluated as functions of the DGP parameters.

- Fourthly, the **speed** of the program must be enhanced as far as possible if an adequate number of replications is to be feasible, especially during a teaching session. The response in PcNaive is to draw on the Ox language. Outcomes at every feasible sample size can be calculated simultaneously, generating a considerable increase in information relevant to investigating finite-sample behaviour and the effects thereon of changes in sample sizes, economizing on the number of experiments needed but at a noticeable cost in computer time. Chapter 14 describes simulation methods, which are discussed in detail in Chapter 14.

- Finally, since **output must be readily comprehensible** both for behaviour between replications and across econometric sample sizes, including inter-method comparisons, PcNaive exploits GiveWin's screen graphics to portray simulation findings. Sampling variability between replications at a given econometric sample size is illustrated by non-parametrically estimated density functions and associated histograms. Conventional numerical estimates of estimator moments, test rejection frequencies etc., are also reported to an output file for later analysis and summarizing. Sample-size variations are reported using plots of biases, standard errors, or estimated sampling standard deviations for changing econometric sample sizes. By copy and paste, GiveWin graphics allow easy contrasts between methods or features (e.g., biases, or standard deviations and standard errors). The tutorials are concerned with the design of experiments and the numerical and graphical output of PcNaive.

1.4 Documentation conventions

The convention for instructions that you should type is that they are shown in Typewriter font. Capitals and lower case are only distinguished as the names of variables in the program and the mathematical formulae you type. Commands on menus, toolbar buttons, and dialog items (buttons, checkboxes etc.) are shown in Sans Serif font.

Equations are numbered as (chapter.number); for example, (8.1) refers to equation 8.1, which is the first equation in Chapter 8. References to sections have the form §chapter.section, for example, §8.1 is Section 8.1 in Chapter 8. Tables and Figures are shown as Figure chapter.number (e.g.) Figure 5.2 for the second figure in Chapter 5. Multiple graphs are numbered from left to right and top to bottom, so (b) is the top-right graph of four, and (c) the bottom left.

1.5 Using PcNaive documentation

The documentation comes in four main parts: Part I contains this prologue and a summary description of the DGPs and models available in PcNaive; Part II provides step by step tutorials to the input and output of PcNaive and asymptotic analysis; Part III considers the use of Monte Carlo methods in econometrics teaching. Part IV considers the Monte Carlo methods and econometrics of PcNaive.

(1) Part II starts with a brief introduction to Monte Carlo analysis in Chapter 3.

(2) The tutorials in Chapters 4 to 8 offer guidance on the experimental formulation procedures and the output interpretation through worked examples.

(3) Part III concerns using PcNaive in econometrics teaching (and, of course, learning). It contains many more examples of analyses made using PcNaive, ranging from the elementary level, through intermediate to advanced econometrics.

(4) Chapter 2 presents a summary of the DGPs, estimators, and tests available in PcNaive.

(5) Chapter 14 describes the more theoretical aspects of Monte Carlo methods in considerable detail.

(6) Chapter 15 describes the use of response surfaces, and Chapter 16 the asymptotic analysis, two important components in reducing Monte Carlo specificity.

(7) File handling and graph printing are all considered in the companion book on GiveWin (Doornik and Hendry, 2001a) so are not reproduced here.

(8) Finally, the book ends with references and indexes.

The appropriate sequence is to first read and follow the examples in the tutorials, consulting the more theoretical chapters when required. Following that we hope that you can use PcNaive productively for your own research or teaching: there is an infinite array of interesting experiments which can be performed with PcNaive

1.6 Citation

To facilitate replication and validation of empirical findings, PcNaive should be cited in all reports and publications involving its application. The appropriate form is to cite the PcNaive book in the list of references.

1.7 World Wide Web

Consult `www.nuff.ox.ac.uk/Users/Doornik/` and `www.oxmetrics.com` for pointers to additional information relevant to the current and future versions of PcNaive.

1.8 Installation and run-time issues

It is recommended that PcNaive is installed to the `packages\PcNaive` folder of your Ox installation. Experiments generated with PcNaive can be saved anywhere on the hard disk.

PcNaive requires Ox Professional version 3.0 or newer. Using PcNaive to design and run an experiment involves the following steps:

- Start PcNaive from inside GiveWin;

- PcNaive creates an Ox program, and saves it to disk;

- PcNaive calls OxRun to run this program;

- OxRun sends all output (text and graphics) to GiveWin.

When only the Console version of Ox is installed `OxRun2.exe` is not available. In that case PcNaive can still design experiments, but they can only be run from the command line (or from OxEdit).

PcNaive expects to find `PcNaiveExe.ox` and `PcNaiveExt.ox` in the same folder as the PcNaive executable (also see Ch. 9).

Chapter 2

The Data Generation Processes and Models of PcNaive

2.1 AR(1) DGP

2.1.1 Data generation process

The AR(1) data generation process is:

$$y_t = \mu + \alpha y_{t-1} + \epsilon_t \text{ with } \epsilon_t \sim \text{IN}\left[0, 1\right], \tag{2.1}$$

where α or μ may be set to zero.

2.1.2 Model

The model is:

$$y_t = \beta_0 + \beta_1 y_{t-1} + u_t \text{ with } u_t \sim \text{IN}\left[0, \sigma^2\right],$$

which is estimated by OLS. Either the constant term or the lagged dependent variable can be omitted.

The sample size is specified as $T_1, T_1+s, T_1+2s, \ldots, T_2$, where the step size s may be zero. The Monte Carlo sample size is automatically adjusted if the model includes a lagged dependent variable.

2.1.3 Estimates and tests

The following estimates and tests can be investigated

- Coefficients – $\widehat{\beta}_0, \widehat{\beta}_1$ (provided they were estimated),
- Standard errors – $\text{SE}_{\widehat{\beta}_0}, \text{SE}_{\widehat{\beta}_1}$ (provided they were estimated),
- Goodness-of-fit – $\widehat{\sigma}^2, R^2$,
- t - tests – $t_{\widehat{\beta}_0=0}, t_{\widehat{\beta}_1=0}$ (provided they were estimated),
- AR1 test, DW – test for AR(1) errors and Durbin–Watson statistic

2.1.4 Plots

- Data – generated data: y_t, $t = 1, \ldots, T$,
- Recursive results – plots of estimates and tests as a function of sample size,
- Histograms – histograms of the estimates and test statistics,
- Set plot frequency – determines how often graphs are created:
  the default frequency is $M/4$, or M when a recursive Monte Carlo is run; it could
  be that a higher frequency is desired when data are graphed.

2.2 Static DGP

2.2.1 Data generation process

The static data generation process is:

$$y_t \quad = \quad \alpha_1 z_{a,t} + \alpha_2 z_{b,t} + \epsilon_t, \qquad \epsilon_t \quad \sim \quad \text{IN}\,[0,1]\,,$$

$$\begin{pmatrix} z_{a,t} \\ z_{b,t} \end{pmatrix} \quad \sim \quad \text{IN}\left[\begin{pmatrix} 0 \\ 0 \end{pmatrix}, \begin{pmatrix} 1 & \rho \\ \rho & 1 \end{pmatrix}\right], \qquad (2.2)$$

where α_1, α_2, or ρ may be set to zero. The regressors can be kept fixed, or recreated in
each replication (stochastic regressors).

2.2.2 Model

The model for the static DGP is:

$$y_t = \beta_0 + \beta_1 z_{a,t} + \beta_2 z_{b,t} + u_t, \quad u_t \sim \text{IN}\,[0,\sigma^2]\,,$$

which is estimated by OLS, and where the constant, $z_{a,t}$ and/or $z_{b,t}$ may be omitted.
The $z_{a,t}$ and $z_{b,t}$ are labelled Za and Zb in the output.

The sample size is specified as $T_1, T_1 + s, T_1 + 2s, \ldots, T_2$, where the step size s
may be zero.

2.2.3 Estimates and tests

This is the same as for the AR(1) DGP, for the same tests, and the estimates $\widehat{\beta}_0, \widehat{\beta}_1, \widehat{\beta}_2$,
provided they are included in the model.

2.2.4 Plots

This is the same as for the AR(1) DGP, for the same tests, and the estimates $\widehat{\beta}_0, \widehat{\beta}_1, \widehat{\beta}_2$,
provided they are included in the model.

2.3 PcNaive and General DGP

2.3.1 Data generation process for PcNaive DGP

The **PcNaive DGP** is a data generation process designed for use in (multivariate) dynamic econometric Monte Carlo experiments:

$$
\begin{aligned}
\mathbf{y}_t &= \mathbf{A}_0\mathbf{y}_t + \mathbf{A}_1\mathbf{y}_{t-1} + \mathbf{A}_2\mathbf{z}_t + \mathbf{a}_3 + \mathbf{A}_5\mathbf{y}_{t-2} + \mathbf{u}_t, \\
\mathbf{u}_t &= \mathbf{B}_0\mathbf{u}_{t-1} + \mathbf{e}_t + \mathbf{B}_1\mathbf{e}_{t-1}, \\
\mathbf{z}_t &= \mathbf{C}_0\mathbf{z}_{t-1} + \mathbf{c}_1 + \mathbf{c}_2 t + \mathbf{v}_t.
\end{aligned}
\tag{2.3}
$$

The vectors $\mathbf{y}_t, \mathbf{u}_t, \mathbf{e}_t$ are $n \times 1$, so that the coefficient matrices $\mathbf{A}_0, \mathbf{A}_1, \mathbf{B}_0, \mathbf{B}_1$ are $n \times n$, and $\mathbf{a}_3$ is $n \times 1$. The $\mathbf{z}_t$ vector is $q \times 1$, making $\mathbf{a}_2$ $n \times q$, $\mathbf{C}_0$ $q \times q$, and $\mathbf{c}_1, \mathbf{c}_2$ $q \times 1$. The zs can be kept fixed between experiments, or regenerated for each experiment.

When $\mathbf{B}_0 = \mathbf{B}_1 = \mathbf{0}$ there are no ARMA errors. When $\mathbf{A}_0 = \mathbf{0}$ the DGP is in reduced form, when also $\mathbf{A}_2 = \mathbf{0}$ the DGP is a VAR(2), and when in addition $\mathbf{A}_5 = \mathbf{0}$ the DGP is a VAR(1).

A distribution for $\mathbf{e}_t$ and $\mathbf{v}_t$ can be specified. Writing ϵ_t for either $\mathbf{e}_t$ or $\mathbf{v}_t$, then:

distribution	parametrization
none	0 (no distribution)
normal (IN)	$\epsilon_{it} \sim \mathsf{N}(\alpha_i, \beta_i) = \mathsf{N}(0, 1) \times \sqrt{\beta_i} + \alpha_i$
multivariate normal (MVN)	$\epsilon_t \sim \mathsf{N}_n(\boldsymbol{\alpha}, \boldsymbol{\beta})$
MVN with correlations	$\epsilon_t \sim \mathsf{N}_n(\boldsymbol{\alpha}, \boldsymbol{\beta})$ with standard deviations on diagonal, correlations on lower diagonal
log normal	$\epsilon_{it} \sim \Lambda(\alpha_i, \beta_i) = \exp\{N(0, 1)\} \times \sqrt{\alpha_i} + \beta_i$
Student-t	$\epsilon_{it} \sim \mathsf{t}(\alpha_i)$
F	$\epsilon_{it} \sim \mathsf{F}(\alpha_i, \beta_i)$
exponential	$\epsilon_{it} \sim \exp(\alpha_i)$
MVN with ARCH	$\epsilon_t \sim \mathsf{N}_n(\mathbf{0}, \boldsymbol{\alpha} + \boldsymbol{\beta}\epsilon_{t-1}\epsilon_{t-1}'\boldsymbol{\beta}')$
MVN with heteroscedasticity	$\mathbf{e}_t \sim \mathsf{N}_n(\mathbf{0}, \boldsymbol{\alpha} + \boldsymbol{\beta}\mathbf{y}_{t-1}\mathbf{y}_{t-i}'\boldsymbol{\beta}')$

The parameters α and β are captured in matrices as follows:

	α_i	α	β_i	β
$\mathbf{e}_t$	$n \times 1$ vector $\mathbf{m}_0$	$n \times n$ matrix $\mathbf{M}_0$	$n \times 1$ vector $\mathbf{s}_0$	$n \times n$ matrix $\mathbf{S}_0$
$\mathbf{v}_t$	$q \times 1$ vector $\mathbf{m}_1$	$q \times q$ matrix $\mathbf{M}_1$	$q \times 1$ vector $\mathbf{s}_1$	$q \times q$ matrix $\mathbf{S}_1$

Initial values for $\mathbf{y}_0$ can be specified.

2.3.1.1 PcNaive DGP in equilibrium-correction form

The DGP can also be formulated as a cointegrated VAR in equilibrium-correction form:

$$\Delta \mathbf{y}_t = \alpha \beta' \begin{pmatrix} \mathbf{y}_{t-1} \\ \mathbf{z}_t \end{pmatrix} + \mathbf{A}_2 \mathbf{z}_t + \mathbf{a}_3 + \mathbf{A}_5^* \Delta \mathbf{y}_{t-1} + \mathbf{u}_t. \tag{2.4}$$

The rank of the cointegrating space must be specified.

Note how in (2.4) the $\mathbf{z}_t$ component enters both the cointegrating space and unrestrictedly. This offers complete flexibility: the zeros in $\mathbf{A}_2$ and β determine what actually happens. For example, setting $\mathbf{A}_2 = \mathbf{0}$ would force all zs into the cointegration space, unless, of course, the corresponding elements of β are also zero, in which case the zs do not enter at all.

2.3.1.2 PcNaive DGP with break

A sample period can be specified over which any of the matrices in the $\mathbf{y}_t$ equation of (2.3) or the $\Delta \mathbf{y}_t$ equation of (2.4) can have different values.

The break period is specified as $T_1^b, \ldots T_2^b$, meaning that the break starts at T_1^b, The first post-break observation is $T_2^b + 1$. For example, when the break period is $[20, 30]$, the break is active over 11 periods.

2.3.2 Data generation process for the General DGP

The **General DGP** is the most general data generation process in PcNaive, and therefore the most complex.

The form of the DGP in mathematical formulation is a reduced-form model:

$$\begin{aligned} \mathbf{y}_t &= \mathbf{\Pi} \mathbf{w}_t + \mathbf{u}_t, \quad t = T_1, \ldots, T_2, \\ \mathbf{z}_t &= \mathbf{C}_0 \mathbf{z}_{t-1} + \mathbf{v}_t, \quad t = T_1, \ldots, T_2. \end{aligned}$$

where $\mathbf{w}$ contains $\mathbf{z}$, r lags of $\mathbf{z}$ and m lags of $\mathbf{y}$:

$$\mathbf{w}_t' = \left(\mathbf{y}_{t-1}', \ldots, \mathbf{y}_{t-m}', \mathbf{z}_t', \ldots, \mathbf{z}_{t-r}' \right).$$

Take $\mathbf{y}_t$ as an $n \times 1$ vector, $\mathbf{z}_t$ as $q \times 1$, and $\mathbf{w}_t$ as $k \times 1$.

The DGP database is constructed as follows:

$0 \ldots s - 1$	initial values for lagged observations, $s \geq \max(1, m, r)$
$T_1 = s \ldots s + d - 1$	space to allow for discarded observations,
$T_1 + d \ldots T_2^*$	remainder of generated data.

The distributions for the error term offer the same choice as the PcNaive DGP.

2.3.3 Models

Models of the PcNaive and general DGP can be estimated by:

(1) single-equation OLS,
(2) single-equation (generalized) instrumental variables,
(3) multiple-equation OLS (including vector autoregressions).

The implementation corresponds to PcGive (see Doornik and Hendry, 2001b). There are four types of variables:

Y endogenous variable: more than one results in a multivariate model, unless additional instruments have been specified,

Z regressor (corresponding to unmarked regressors in the model formulation dialog),

U unrestricted regressor,

A additional instruments for IV estimation.

The distinction between **U** and **Z** only matters for cointegration tests.

The estimated quantities are split into 'estimates' and 'tests'. For the former, the output includes means, standard errors, biases, etc. For the latter, the output consists of the first four moments, rejection frequencies and critical values.

In case of recursive Monte Carlo, the experiment is run for sample sizes $T = T_1, \ldots, T_2$. The Monte Carlo sample size is automatically adjusted to allow for lagged variables in the model.

2.3.4 Estimates

Let n denote the number of equations in the econometric model, k the number of regressors, and T the sample size.

- Coefficients
  The nk estimated coefficients.
- Standard errors
  The nk estimated standard errors of the coefficients.
- Goodness of fit
  If $n = 1$: $\widehat{\sigma}^2$ and R^2.
  If $n > 1$: $\widehat{\Omega}_{ii}$ for $i = 1, \ldots, n$ (the residual variance for each equation).
- Cointegration eigenvalues
  The eigenvalues μ_i, $i = 1, \ldots, n$ from the reduced-rank estimation.

2.3.5 Tests

- t-values
  The nk estimated t-values for all coefficients.

- AR1 test

  F-test on first-order residual autocorrelation. This is the F form of the test by Breusch (1978) and Godfrey (1978). When $n > 1$, it is the multivariate version, see Doornik (1996). For $n = 1$, the Durbin–Watson is also computed.

- Normality test

  The Doornik and Hansen (1994) test for normality, which is approximately $\chi^2(2n)$ distributed under the null hypothesis.

- Forecast Chow tests

  When the model is estimated up to T, this tests for constancy up to $T_2 + H$. Since $T_2 + H \geq T$, this is called the forecast Chow tests.

  When $n = 1$ the test is:

  $$\frac{(RSS_{T_2+H} - RSS_T)\,(T - k)}{RSS_T\,(T_2 + H - T)} \sim \mathsf{F}(T_2 + H - T, T - k).$$

  For $n > 1$ the vector form is reported, see Doornik and Hendry (2001b).

  Note that for the last sample size (or when the Monte Carlo is not recursive) and the number of forecasts is zero ($H = 0$): $T = T_2$ and the test is zero, with p-value one.

- Breakpoint Chow tests

  When the model is estimated up to T, this tests for insample constancy from $T_1 \leq T$. Since this is insample, it is called the break-point Chow tests.

  When $n = 1$ the test is:

  $$\frac{(RSS_T - RSS_{T_1})\,(T_1 - k)}{RSS_T\,(T - T_1)} \sim \mathsf{F}(T, T_1 - k).$$

  For $n > 1$ the vector form is reported, see Doornik and Hendry (2001b).

  Note that when the Monte Carlo is not recursive: $T = T_1$ and the test is zero, with p-value one.

- Co/integration tests

  - When $n = 1$ this reports the ECM or ADF test, depending on the presence of other regressors. Let $q + 1$ be the number of distinct variables (q is the number of regressors not counting any lagged regressors and not counting the constant term or trend). The model for estimation is written as:

    $$a(L)y_t = b(L)x_t + \ldots + u_t,$$

    which can be written in equilibrium-correction form as:

    $$\Delta y_t = [a(1) - 1]\,y_{t-1} + a^*(L)\Delta y_{t-1} + b(L)x_t + \ldots + u_t,$$

    where $a(1)$ is the sum of the coefficients on the lagged dependent variable. The test statistic is the t-value of $a(1) - 1$. When $q = 1$ (no other regressors) this is the ADF(s) test, where s is the number of lagged ys minus one (i.e. the number of lagged differences). When $q > 1$ this is the PcGive unit-root test for cointegration, denoted ECM(q). The 5% critical values of this test are based on a meta response surface for the results from Ericsson and MacKinnon (1999).[1]

Note that the test is sensitive to the treatment of deterministic terms, which is noted, e.g. ADF(1;c) when a constant is included as a regressor, and ADF(1;ct) for a constant and trend. There are no p-values available for this test, and the returned pseudo p-value is 0.0 when the test rejects, and 1.0 when it accepts.

– When $n > 1$ the cointegration test is based on the maximum likelihood procedure of Johansen (1988). The test statistic is the trace test H($p \leq i$) for $i = 0, \ldots, n - 1$. There are five versions, based on the treatment of deterministic terms. In the notation of Doornik, Hendry and Nielsen (1998) and Doornik and Hendry (2001b):

Hypothesis	Constant	Trend
$H_{ql}(p)$	unrestricted	unrestricted
$H_l(p)$	unrestricted	restricted
$H_{lc}(p)$	unrestricted	none
$H_c(p)$	restricted	none
$H_z(p)$	none	none

The terms unrestricted/restricted refers to the classification in model formulation, which determines whether a variable is restricted to the cointegrating space or not. The asymptotic p-values are based on the approximations in Doornik (1998).

- Cointegration (asymptotic)
This uses the generated u_t to compute the critical values for the maximum likelihood test for cointegration based on the discrete equivalents of the Brownian motions (see e.g. Johansen, 1995, Ch. 15, Simulations and Tables). The repor-

---

[1] Meta-response surface for quantiles Q when $q > 1$, $d = 0, 1, 2$:

$$Q(T_i) = \widehat{\theta}_\infty + \widehat{\theta}_1 [T_i - (2q - 1) - d]^{-1} + u_i,$$

$$
\begin{aligned}
\widehat{\theta}_\infty^{5\%} &= -2.056 - 0.535d(1 - q/20) - 0.343q(1 - q/40) \\
\widehat{\theta}_\infty^{1\%} &= \widehat{\theta}_\infty^{5\%} - 0.607 \\
\widehat{\theta}_1^{5\%} &= 7.09 - 0.483k + 3.64 * \widehat{\theta}_\infty^{5\%} * (1 - q/10) \\
\widehat{\theta}_1^{1\%} &= 13.8 - 0.447k + 6.06 * \widehat{\theta}_\infty^{1\%} * (1 - q/20)
\end{aligned}
$$

with $d = 0$ for no deterministic terms, $d = 1$ for a constant, and $d = 2$ for a trend. For the ADF test, $q = 1$, the values for θ_j are taken from the relevant tables in Ericsson and MacKinnon (1999).

ted tests are the trace and maximum eigenvalue statistics for the treatment of the constant and trend adopted in the estimating model. No p-values are available.
- Cointegration (cond. on 1)
  This is the trace test for cointegration, but the asymptotic distribution is modified to assume that it is conditional on one stationary exogenous regressor. The p-values are based on Boswijk and Doornik (1999).
- Cointegration (cond. on 2)
  As above, but conditional on two regressors.

2.3.6 Plots

- Histograms of estimates
  Histogram and non-parametrically estimated density of the selected estimates.
- Histograms of tests
  Histogram and non-parametrically estimated density of the selected test statistics.
- Rec. mean of estimates
  The mean of the estimates at the sample sizes of the recursive Monte Carlo, shown with ± 2MCSD bands. If the standard errors are also simulated, the ± 2ESE bands are also shown.
- Rec. bias of estimates
  The mean bias of the estimates at the sample sizes of the recursive Monte Carlo.
- Rec. MCSD/RMSE of estimates
  The MCSD and RMSE of the estimates at the sample sizes of the recursive Monte Carlo.
- Rec. mean of tests
  The mean of the test statistics at the sample sizes of the recursive Monte Carlo.
- Rec. rejection frequencies
  The rejection frequencies at the right tail of the test statistics at the sample sizes of the recursive Monte Carlo, at user-specified p-values.
- Rec. critical values
  The critical values at the right tail of the test statistics at the sample sizes of the recursive Monte Carlo, at user-specified p-values.
- Generated data
  The generated y_t.
- Standardized data
  The generated y_t in deviation from its mean and divided by the standard deviation.

Part II

PcNaive Tutorials

Chapter 3

Introduction to Monte Carlo Experimentation

3.1 PcNaive

Monte Carlo is a general technique for solving a (deterministic) mathematical problem by substituting a stochastic problem which has the same solution, then solving the latter by simulation experiments. For example, one might simulate the distribution of the ratio of the sample mean to its standard deviation rather than determine it analytically. It is a useful approach when the desired theoretical solution is analytically intractable, or the labour costs involved in solution are high relative to the capital cost of computer simulation. Such a situation occurs regularly when trying to evaluate high dimensional integrals. Since the expectations, and higher moments, of estimators, or the powers of tests, are integrals or functions thereof, Monte Carlo simulation has proved valuable in econometric research. In a teaching context, Monte Carlo has proved useful for developing a quantitative understanding of the finite-sample properties of econometric estimators and test statistics, and of the relation of theoretical results to practical situations. The methodology of Monte Carlo experimentation is exposited in Hendry (1984) and in Chapter 14 below; Sowey (1973) lists many applications of Monte Carlo to econometrics problems.

This prologue introduces the Monte Carlo simulation and asymptotic-analysis program PcNaive, and describes its structure, functioning, simulation methodology, model class, estimation and test capabilities, and output modes. The focus of the program is on the finite-sample behaviour of estimators and tests for systems of linear dynamic equations, so considerable emphasis is placed on how such properties change with the sample size. PcNaive (the acronym from **N**umerical **A**nalysis of **I**nstrumental **V**ariables **E**stimators) designs simulation experiments using a menu-driven approach. Then the program generates Ox code (see Doornik, 2001) which is run by OxRun, and passes text and graphical output to GiveWin (see Doornik and Hendry, 2001a). In addition, PcNaive computes asymptotic analyses of the same statistical methods, but restricted to stationary stochastic processes, or the stationary representation of cointegrated systems. The discussion in this book covers the use of PcNaive for both teaching and research.

For details of earlier incarnations of PcNaive, see Hendry and Trivedi (1972), Hendry and Harrison (1974), Hendry and Srba (1980), Hendry and Neale (1987), and Hendry, Neale and Ericsson (1991).

3.2 Monte Carlo

A Monte Carlo experiment to study the finite-sample properties of an econometric method of interest involves generating random samples of artificial data from a statistical mechanism which is fully specified numerically, using random numbers in place of the random variables of the theory. The aim is to infer the (unknown) theoretical properties of the method under study from the empirical distribution obtained by repeatedly applying that method to the artificial samples. If directly implemented as just described, the method is usually called distribution sampling. This approach to evaluating features of a statistical distribution by representing it numerically and drawing observations from that numerical representation has been used in statistics from an early date (see Student, 1908, Yule, 1926, and Orcutt and Cochrane, 1949, *inter alia*). For example, the standardized normal density (denoted $X \sim \mathsf{N}[0,1]$) is represented by the analytical formula:

$$\mathsf{f}_\mathsf{x}\left(x\right) = \left(\sqrt{2\pi}\right)^{-1} \exp\left(-\tfrac{1}{2}x^2\right),$$

where $\mathsf{f}_\mathsf{x}\left(x\right)$ denotes the density. Equally, the standardized normal can be represented by a table of numbers which records the numerical values of $\mathsf{f}_\mathsf{x}(x)$ corresponding to each value of $x \in (-\infty, \infty)$. To investigate the distribution of the mean $\bar{x}$ of random samples of (say) T observations from that distribution, one could analytically calculate:

$$\mathsf{E}\left[\bar{x}\right] = T^{-1}\sum_{t=1}^{T}\int_{-\infty}^{\infty} x_t \mathsf{f}_\mathsf{x}(x_t)\mathrm{d}x_t \ \text{ where } \ \bar{x} = T^{-1}\sum_{t=1}^{T} x_t;$$

(where $\mathsf{E}[\cdot]$ denotes expectation) and so on for higher moments. While feasible for the normal, this is often a daunting, and sometimes intractable, task. Alternatively, one could draw a large number of random samples of size T from a table of the standardized normal density, and calculate their mean, or plot the resulting distribution etc. Numerically representing a known distribution and randomly sampling from it is an important part of most Monte Carlo experiments (as named by Metropolis and Ulam, 1949).

Monte Carlo experiments can greatly extend the set of statistical generating mechanisms which can be investigated as compared to only using mathematical analysis. Against this, one must balance the inherent imprecision and specificity of simulation. The former (imprecision) derives from the very use of random sampling, since different outcomes would result on re-conducting the experiment using different random numbers: Chapter 14 discusses methods of minimizing imprecision. The latter (specificity) is due to the need to represent the data generation process (DGP) numerically, so only a finite set of parameter values can ever be investigated. To reduce specificity, one must formulate a DGP of sufficient generality to cover the essential features of the econometric theory, with a parameter space $(\Psi : \mathcal{T}) = \{(\psi : T) | \psi \in \Psi : T \in \mathcal{T}\}$, where Ψ denotes the parameter space of the DGP, and $\mathcal{T}$ is the set of econometric sample sizes of interest. Then a range of experiments must be undertaken to cover this space. Finally, the (often) voluminous outcomes of simulation experiments must be efficiently summarized as discussed in Chapter 14 (also see Hammersley and Handscomb, 1964, p.59, Hendry, 1984, and Ripley, 1987).

In finite-sample studies, the main interest is in the impact of the sample size T, and how changes in T influence the behaviour of tests and estimation techniques for any given point $\psi \in \Psi$, so this aspect will be a major focus of the discussion. The role of Monte Carlo in a live teaching environment is also described. Relative to earlier releases, PcNaive now offers great research potential, since there is a comprehensive programming facility via Ox (see Doornik, 2001), and hence it is not limited to the range of pre-programmed routines offered. The acronym PcNaive has become increasingly inapt, although the present version does not automatically implement within-experiment variance reduction methods, and estimation is limited to linear models. Nevertheless, as the remainder of this chapter outlines, the feasible range of experiments is extremely large. Moreover, the structure of the program allows additional features to be incorporated as users desire.

3.3 The data generation process

The basic DGP incorporated in PcNaive is defined by a linear system of simultaneous stochastic dynamic equations. Let y_t denote an $n \times 1$ vector of endogenous variables and z_t an $m \times 1$ vector of strongly exogenous variables, then the system can be a nonstationary non-Gaussian process, with trends, ARCH, autoregressive-moving average errors, or measurement errors, and a wide range of possible structural breaks.

For the first tutorials, a simple version of the general DGP is used:

$$y_t = \mu + \alpha y_{t-1} + \epsilon_t, \text{ with } \epsilon_t \sim \text{IN}[0,1]. \tag{3.1}$$

This DGP is a simple autoregressive process, with a constant term, and errors which have a standard normal distribution. The parameters in (3.1) define the design space: $\{\psi\} = \{\mu, \alpha\}$.

The Monte Carlo DGP represents the econometric theory DGP with two differences. First, the parameters (ψ, T) of the latter become the design variables of the former in that the user defines the numerical values of all the DGP parameters. This selection should be made to enhance simulation efficiency by covering the range of parameter values of likely interest. Secondly, the random variables of the theory are simulated by random numbers intended to mimic their distributional properties, see §14.9.

3.4 Simulation methods

Having defined the problem of interest, numerical simulation can proceed, possibly involving multiple jobs, where each job comprises a different point $(\psi : T)$ in the parameter space. Independent random numbers are used for generating $\{\epsilon_t\}$, and hence for constructing $\{y_t\}$ from equation (3.1) above.

To focus on the effects of changing sample size when studying finite-sample behaviour, the option of recursive Monte Carlo is invaluable. This simultaneously computes outcomes at all sample sizes up to the largest of interest. There is a significant increase in cost over a single sample size, and by using common random numbers, recursive Monte Carlo methods can be viewed as a technique for variance reduction by minimizing uncertainty between the outcomes at successive sample sizes (see Ch.14). Less obviously, recursive estimation linked to graphical output also helps reduce the consumption costs entailed in the analysis of Monte Carlo results, by providing graphical analogues of response surfaces for fixed ψ but varying intensively over T. The accompanying asymptotic analysis, discussed in Chapter 16, is designed to assist in formulating response surfaces which link numerical findings to asymptotic analyses, as discussed in Chapter 15. In a classroom environment, such techniques aid the demonstration of theoretical results. Further, prior to conducting a long set of experiments on a stationary DGP, the probability limits of parameter estimators, or local asymptotic approximations to the powers of test statistics can be calculated to guide the experimental design. In post-experiment analyses, population outcomes also act as inter-experiment controls to reduce the imprecision of response surface estimates (see Ch. 14, Hendry, 1973, 1982, and Ericsson, 1986).

3.5 The output of PcNaive

During replications, output information about the experiment in progress is sent to GiveWin, including continuously-updated information on coefficient distributions, any error messages, and graphical output.

The output of PcNaive is both numerical (e.g. biases, standard errors, plims of estimators, and so on), and graphical (e.g. histograms of frequency distributions, recursively-computed biases across sample sizes, constancy-test rejection frequencies). Averages across replications of estimators and test statistics are plotted against the associated sample size, as well as pictorial histograms of the distributions of estimators and tests across replications at a given sample size: interpolations approximating the density functions can be fit. All output during a simulation is written to GiveWin, so this can be viewed, and the DGP or model reviewed as needed. Recursive graphical output is easily 'copy and pasted'.

While replications proceed, the graphics screen can be explained in a classroom, or checked for the state of an experiment.

Chapter 4

Tutorial for an $\mathsf{IN}[\mu, \sigma^2]$ Process

4.1 Introduction

This chapter walks through the input and simulation output for the $\mathsf{IN}\left[\mu, \sigma^2\right]$ process, and discusses the interpretation of the output. This simple stochastic process is also used as an illustration in Chapter 14. To define the Monte Carlo (MC) experiment, we need to formulate a data generation process (DGP), and an econometric model which is applied to that DGP.

- The **data generation process** is:

$$y_t = \mu + \epsilon_t \text{ with } \epsilon_t \sim \mathsf{IN}\left[0, \sigma_\epsilon^2\right],$$

  where $\mu \in (-\infty, \infty)$, $\sigma_\epsilon^2 > 0$, and $t = 1, \ldots, T$.
- The **econometric relationship of interest** is:

$$y_t = \mu + u_t \text{ with } u_t \sim \mathsf{IN}\left[0, \sigma^2\right],$$

  which is the same as the DGP.

The objective of the Monte Carlo analysis here is understanding the finite-sample properties of the OLS estimator of μ (with σ^2 assumed unknown), which is the sample mean of y_t:

$$\bar{y} = T^{-1} \sum_{t=1}^{T} y_t.$$

The Monte Carlo design variables are $\psi = (\mu, \sigma^2)'$ and the econometric sample size is T. We consider a single experiment with $(\mu, \sigma^2) = (6, 1)$ and $T = 50$. Notice that there is one 'invariant' of the experiment, namely μ/σ, such that the 'same' results should be obtained at all values of μ and σ corresponding to the same μ/σ (e.g. $\psi = (6, 1)$ and $(12, 4)$). Of course, this claim itself can be checked by experiments with the same random numbers, at appropriate μ, σ combinations.

4.2 Starting PcNaive

Following successful installation, the most convenient way to start PcNaive is from the GiveWin workspace, where it will be listed with any other modules that you may have installed:

The PcNaive main window is quite simple. The top row of four buttons are used to create new Monte Carlo experiments. The different options will be explored in the tutorials. The next row is used to

- Open an experiment that has been created previously,
- Edit an experiment that has been newly created or opened,
- Run an experiment,
- or Exit PcNaive.

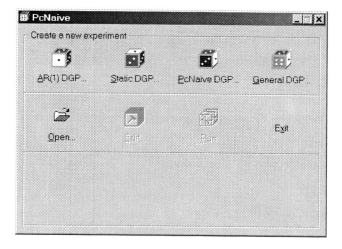

4.3 Designing the IN$[\mu, \sigma^2]$ experiment

In this section we shall create a new experiment by entering all the necessary design parameters Click on AR(1) DGP to see:

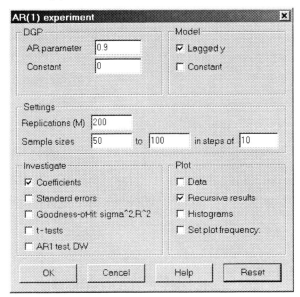

This implements a simple autoregressive DGP, discussed in more detail in Chapter 6. The default settings, as shown in the capture above, correspond to:

- for the DGP:

$$y_t = 0.9y_{t-1} + \epsilon_t, \quad \text{with } \epsilon_t \sim \text{IN}\,[0, 1],$$

- with econometric model:

$$y_t = \alpha y_{t-1} + u_t, \quad \text{with } u_t \sim \text{IN}\left[0, \sigma^2\right].$$

Change design of the dialog to the IN$[6, \sigma^2]$ experiment by:

- setting AR parameter to 0 and Constant to 6 in the DGP panel;
- deselecting Lagged y and select Constant in the Model panel.

The settings are shown in the capture below:

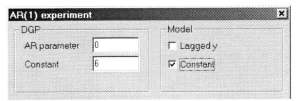

and correspond to:

- DGP:

$$y_t = 6 + \epsilon_t, \quad \text{with } \epsilon_t \sim \mathsf{IN}\,[0, 1]\,,$$

- econometric model:

$$y_t = \mu + u_t, \text{ with } u_t \sim \mathsf{IN}\,\left[0, \sigma^2\right].$$

The remaining options control the number of replications, sample size and output:

- Replications sets M, the number of MC experiments. Change this to 100.
- Sample sizes sets the sample sizes in the form

Sample sizes T_1 to T_2 in steps of s,

  corresponding to $T_1, T_1 + s, T_1 + 2s, \ldots, T_2$. Here only one sample size of 50 is required, so set both T_1 and T_2 to 50 (the in steps of step size will be ignored by PcNaive in that case).
- Investigate determines the objects of study of the experiment:
    - Coefficients – $\widehat{\mu}$,
    - Standard errors– $\text{SE}_{\widehat{\mu}}$,
    - Goodness-of-fit – $\widehat{\sigma}^2$, R^2,
    - t-tests – $t_{\widehat{\mu}=0}$,
    - AR1 test, DW – test for AR(1) errors and Durbin–Watson statistic.
- Plot determines the graphical output created by PcNaive:
    - Data – generated data.
    - Recursive results – plots as a function of sample size,
    - Histograms – histograms of the M generated statistics,
    - Set plot frequency – determines how often graphs are created (the default frequency is $M/4$, or M when a recursive Monte Carlo is run; it could be that a higher frequency is desired when data are graphed).

Although graphs are often the best way to present Monte Carlo results, we will first look at the numerical output only. Therefore deselect Recursive. The remainder of the dialog should look like:

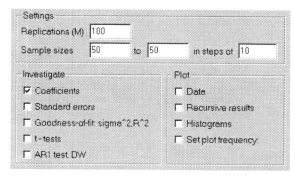

4.4 Saving the IN$[\mu, \sigma^2]$ experiment

Pressing OK in the dialog will prompt you to save the new experiment in an Ox file. We suggest you use the file name tut1.ox, and either save it in the PcNaive folder, or your own work folder.

When the file is saved (we used the file name tutmean01, which is already in your PcNaive folder) the summary of the experiment is listed in the third panel on the PcNaive main window:

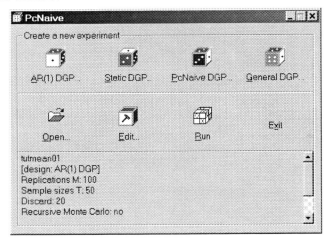

The summary starts with the filename, followed by the type of experiment, and then M, T, etc.

4.5 Running the IN$[\mu, \sigma^2]$ experiment

Press the Run button on the PcNaive main window to run the Monte Carlo experiment. If you haven't started GiveWin yet, it should start automatically. The output appears in GiveWin in a window called tut1.out (provided you named the experiment tut1.ox).

4.6 Output from the IN$[\mu, \sigma^2]$ experiment

For this process, many exact results are known, and they are mentioned here in order to help interpret the Monte Carlo simulations. In more complicated experiments, only (e.g.) asymptotic results may be known, but they may be used in much the same way. The primary difference is that, for this experiment, closeness of the theoretical and Monte Carlo results confirms the validity of the random number generator (and that we didn't get a bad set of random number draws — you shall see below that in our first example we happened to get an extremely good draw), whereas closeness of asymptotic and Monte Carlo results points to the importance of the former in explaining the latter (and so in explaining finite-sample behaviour).

The output appears in an instant, and the components are discussed in turn. The first few lines show that Ox was used to run the experiment, and shows the version number, the time and date when the results were generated, as well as the name of the file which was used to create the results:

```
Ox version 3.00 (Windows) (C) J.A. Doornik, 1994-2001
PcNaive 2.0 experiment started on 26-02-2001 at 12:47:17
PcFiml package version 1.00, object created on 26-02-2001
PcNaive run: D:\Ox\packages\PcNaive\tutmean01.ox
```

The next block gives the settings for the DGP:

```
---- PcNaive (2.00) DGP ----
y is (1 x 1), z is (0 x 1) and fixed.

y[t] = e[t] + a3
a3 =
       6.0000

e ~ N(0,1)
20 observations discarded
```

Followed by the econometric model:

```
---- System estimation by OLS ----
The available estimation sample is 1 - 50 (T=50)
Ya            lag 0 status Y
Constant      lag 0
```

It is always useful to check if this corresponds to the intended design. There are no additional regressors in the DGP (called Zs), making z a 0 by 1 matrix. By default, 20 experiments are discarded. This means that $T + 20$ observations are generated from the DGP, but the first 20 are thrown away. Here that is unnecessary, but when the DGP has a (stationary) lagged dependent variable, it reduces the effect of starting values.

Finally, the outcome from the experiment is listed, with the amount of time it took:

```
---- PcNaive Monte Carlo results ----
T=50, M=100, seed=-1 (common)

moments of estimates
                     mean            MCSD
Constant            5.9994         0.12821

biases of estimates
                 mean bias          MCSE           RMSE    true value
Constant        -0.00061652      0.012821        0.12821      6.0000

Total time for experiment: 0.09
```

T and M are the sample size and number of replications. The seed is set to -1, indicating that the default seed is used every time the experiment is run. This is useful, because the same results will obtain every time.[1]

Section 14.2 considers this experiment in quite some detail. Here we wish to relate the generated output to the results in that section. Each of the $i = 1, \ldots, M$ replications generated data and run ordinary least squares (OLS) on the $T = 50$ observations to obtain an estimate of μ. This gives $\widehat{\mu}_1, \ldots, \widehat{\mu}_{100}$. To simplify notation we write $m_1, \ldots, m_M$ for these outcomes.

The output is constructed from this as follows, when μ is the true parameter:

mean	$\overline{m} = M^{-1} \sum_{i=1}^{M} m_i,$
MCSD	$\widehat{\sigma}_m = \left\{ M^{-1} \sum_{i=1}^{M} (m_i - \overline{m})^2 \right\}^{1/2},$
mean bias	$\overline{m} - \mu,$
MCSE	$\widehat{\sigma}_{\overline{m}} = M^{-1/2} \widehat{\sigma}_m,$
RMSE	$\left\{ M^{-1} \sum_{i=1}^{M} (m_i - \mu)^2 \right\}^{\frac{1}{2}} = \left\{ (\text{MCSD})^2 + (\text{mean bias})^2 \right\}^{\frac{1}{2}},$

where RMSE is the root of the mean squared error. The *Monte Carlo standard deviation* (MCSD) is the standard deviation of the mean.

In this very simple example, exact (analytical) finite-sample results are available. Because the error ϵ_t is IN$[0, 1]$, $\mu = 6$, and $T = 50$, then the estimator $\overline{y}$ of μ is exactly distributed as IN$[6, 1/50]$. Thus, the exact finite-sample bias of the estimator is zero, and the estimated bias of $\overline{y}$ (which is the Monte Carlo sample mean of $\overline{y}$ across the $M = 100$ replications) should be insignificant.

The standard error of the estimated bias is $(1/[TM])^{1/2} = 0.0141$, and measures the uncertainty with which the bias is estimated. This is called the *Monte Carlo standard error* (MCSE): repeating the entire experiment several times should yield estimates of μ with ± 2MCSE 95% of the time. The standard deviation of the estimated bias, which is $(1/T)^{1/2} = 0.141$, and measures the variability of the bias $\overline{y} - 6$ as estimated from one Monte Carlo replication to the next.

Finally, because the (theoretical) bias is zero, the RMSE of the bias should be the same as its standard deviation. Numerically, the theoretical (exact finite-sample) values and the simulation results are close, despite the relatively small number of replications M. Statistically, they are insignificantly different from each other, to the extent that we can assess that (e.g., for the bias).

4.7 Extended IN$[\mu, \sigma^2]$ experiment

Select AR(1) DGP, enter the same design as before, but now including t-tests and Standard errors. Run the new experiment, to obtain (the goodness-of-fit statistics will

---

[1]Some computer programs might use the time and date to create a different seed every time the program is run. That is useful for cryptographic purposes, but less so for MC (and scientific experiments in general), where it is important to be able to replicate previous results.

be discussed later):

```
moments of test statistics
                        mean       std.dev     skewness   ex.kurtosis
t-Constant             43.332       5.0041       0.53968      0.44517

critical values (two sided: left tail quantiles)
                        2.5%
t-Constant             34.884

critical values (two sided: right tail quantiles)
                        2.5%
t-Constant             52.961

rejection frequencies
                         5%
t-Constant             1.0000
[ASE]                  0.021794

moments of estimates
                        mean        MCSD
Constant               5.9994      0.12821
ESE[Constant]          0.14017     0.015254

biases of estimates
                    mean bias       MCSE          RMSE     true value
Constant           -0.00061652     0.012821      0.12821     6.0000
ESE[Constant]       0.14017        0.0015254     0.14100     0.00000
```

The last line lists the average over Monte Carlo replications of the *estimated standard error* (ESE). With one regressor it is the square root of $\hat{\sigma}^2 (\sum_{t=1}^{T} x_t^2)^{-1}$, as well as its standard deviation. Since $E[\hat{\sigma}^2] = 1$ and $x_t = 1$, $t = 1, \ldots T$ is fixed, the (approximate) theoretical mean of the ESE is $(1/T)^{1/2} = 0.141$, which here is also the standard deviation of the estimator.[2] The estimated mean ESE is within two standard errors of this value.

This table also lists the mean and standard deviation of the t-statistic, and the nominal 2.5% critical values. This test is two-sided, with 2.5% rejection in the lower tail, and 2.5% in the upper tail. This corresponds to the 2.5% and 97.5% percentiles from the M computed t-statistics. As explained below, this should be compared to a table of the non-central t-distribution.

The second part gives the percentage rejection frequency at a 5% nominal critical value. This is computed as follows: for each replication, a p-value is calculated from the t(49) distribution for the observed t-statistic (remember: this is a two sided test). The rejection frequency is the percentage of replications with a p-value less than 5%. Here that equals one, indicating that the constant term was significant in all replications. This investigates the *power* of the test. The ASE is explained in §6.2.2.

---

[2]Note that the true value for the ESE is set to zero in the output, which of course is not correct. As a consequence, the RMSE and mean bias have been computed around zero.

Two types of t-statistic could be examined, one for testing $\mu = 0$ and the other for testing $\mu = \mu_0$ where μ_0 is the true value ($\mu_0 = 6$ here). The latter is not listed in the output. For the former, noting that $E[\bar{y}] = 6$ and that $E[\text{ESE}] \approx 0.141$, we have:

$$E[t_{\mu=0}] = E\left[\frac{\bar{y}}{\text{ESE}}\right] \approx \frac{E[\bar{y}]}{E[\text{ESE}]} = 42.4.$$

This is the (approximate) non-centrality of $t_{\mu=0}$ and implies a very high (virtually 100%) rejection frequency. The simulation results match the theoretical results closely.

The second statistic, $t_{\mu=6}$, is a central t-statistic with 49 degrees of freedom, and so has a standard deviation of essentially unity and a rejection frequency of approximately 5%. Note that, for an underlying % rejection rate, the standard error of the corresponding observed rejection frequency is 2% for $M = 100$.

To investigate the *size* of the t test, rerun the experiment with $\mu = 0$ in the DGP. For $M = 1000$:

```
moments of test statistics
                      mean         std.dev        skewness    ex.kurtosis
t-Constant        -0.064726        0.99554       -0.086697      -0.041410

critical values (two sided: left tail quantiles)
                      2.5%
t-Constant         -1.9882

critical values (two sided: right tail quantiles)
                      2.5%
t-Constant          1.8266

rejection frequencies
                       5%
t-Constant         0.042000
[ASE]              0.0068920

moments of estimates
                      mean           MCSD
Constant         -0.0091319       0.13863
ESE[Constant]     0.14088         0.014422

biases of estimates
                   mean bias        MCSE           RMSE       true value
Constant         -0.0091319      0.0043838        0.13893       0.00000
ESE[Constant]     0.14088        0.00045608       0.14161       0.00000
```

Remember that the t-test is a two-sided test: it rejects both for large negative and large positive values.

4.8 Graphical output

At a single sample size T, two types of graphs are available:

- Data
- Histograms

If there are no recursive graphs, the graphs are updated four times during the experiment: at $M/4$, $M/2$, $3M/4$ and M. The data graphs just plot the generated y variables. The histograms draw histograms and estimated densities of the investigated statistics. For example when $M = 1000$ and Coefficients is selected, the last graph will show the distribution of the 1000 generated values for $\widehat{\mu}_i$.

Design the experiment as follows:

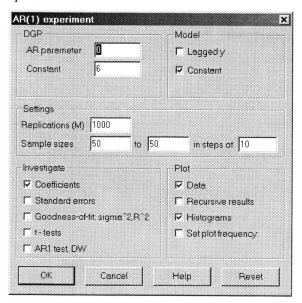

to see a graph as in Fig. 4.1.

4.8.1 Recursive Monte Carlo

Recursive Monte Carlo adds graphs which are a function of the sample size. Say we have two sample sizes, T_1 and T_2, each using M replications. Then we have the histograms at each sample size. In addition, we have $\widehat{\mu}(T = T_1)$ and $\widehat{\mu}(T = T_2)$ which can be graphed against T. Especially when only asymptotic distributions are used, this type of graphs shows the speed at which the asymptotic values are reached.

Adjust the previous experiment by selecting sample size from 10 to 100 in steps of 10, for Plot mark Recursive results only, and Investigate Coefficients and Standard errors. With 1000 replications the result should be as in Fig. 4.2, showing the simulated mean with standard error bands based on ± 2MCSD as well as ± 2ESE.

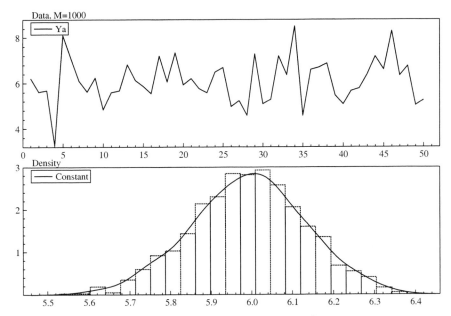

Figure 4.1   Data underlying $\widehat{\mu}_{1000}$ and histogram of $\widehat{\mu}_i$, $i = 1, \ldots, 1000$.

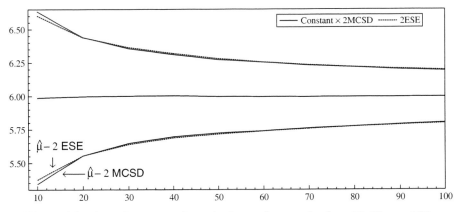

Figure 4.2   Sample mean and standard error for sample sizes $10, 20, \ldots, 100$.

Chapter 5

Tutorial on the Static DGP

5.1 Introduction

This chapter extends the previous set of experiments by adding regressors to the mean. Initially we concentrate on static regression models, where the analysis is simpler than for dynamic models, which have a lagged dependent variable as regressor. The steps taken in this chapter can be related to the discussion in §11.6 — §11.11.

- Initially, the **data generation process** is:

$$y_t = \beta x_t + \epsilon_t \text{ with } \epsilon_t \sim \text{IN}[0, 1].$$

- The **econometric relationship of interest** is:

$$y_t = \beta x_t + u_t \text{ with } u_t \sim \text{IN}[0, \sigma^2],$$

    which corresponds to the DGP.

The objective is understanding the finite sample properties of the OLS estimator $\widehat{\beta}$ of β, which is:

$$\widehat{\beta} = \frac{\sum_{t=1}^{T} x_t y_t}{\sum_{t=1}^{T} x_t^2}. \tag{5.1}$$

The Monte Carlo **design variables** are $\psi = (\beta, \sigma_\epsilon^2)'$ and the econometric sample size is T. We consider a single experiment with $(\beta, \sigma_\epsilon^2) = (1, 1)$ and $T = 60$.

5.2 Designing the Static experiment

We assume that you have already worked your way through the previous chapter. The same DGP/model editor is used here, so formulating the experiment will be straightforward.

Start PcNaive, and click on Static DGP: the top part of the dialog is used to formulate the DGP and the model, the middle part controls sample size, and the number of

34

replications (M), while the remainder controls the output. In the DGP set the coefficient of Regressor 1 to 1, and the other two DGP parameters to 0 (which is the default). In the model, select Regressor 1 only. Next, set the starting and ending sample size to 60, the number of replications to 1000, and remove the tick in front of Renew Z every replication. Under Investigate, select Coefficients, Standard errors, and Goodness-of-fit, and deactivate all Plot options. The completed dialog is:

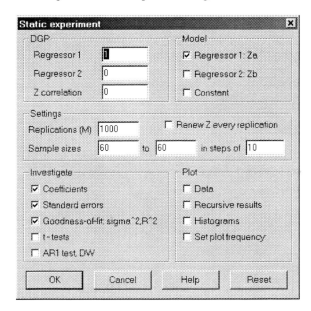

Click on OK, and save this file (as before, a version is already in your PcNaive folder under the name tutstatic01, so you may wish to use a different name). Then click on Run to do the experiment, which will only take a little while.

5.2.1 Output from the experiment

5.2.1.1 Description of the experiment

The output commences with a summary of the DGP and the model:

```
---- PcNaive (2.00) DGP ----
y is (1 x 1), z is (2 x 1) and fixed.

y[t] = e[t] + A2 z[t]
A2 =
        1.0000        0.00000

e ~ N(0,1)

z[t] = v[t]
```

```
v ~ MVN(0,I)
20 observations discarded

---- System estimation by OLS ----
The available estimation sample is 1 - 60 (T=60)
Ya              lag 0 status Y
Za              lag 0

---- PcNaive Monte Carlo results ----
T=60, M=1000, seed=-1 (common)
```

This repeats the intended design:

$$\text{DGP:} \quad y_t = 1 \times x_t + 0 \times z_t + \epsilon_t \text{ with } \epsilon_t \sim \text{IN}[0,1],$$
$$\text{Model:} \quad y_t = \beta x_t + u_t \text{ with } u_t \sim \text{IN}[0,\sigma^2].$$

A few remarks are in order:

- The static DGP always generates two regressors, called Za and Zb. In this case, the second has coefficient zero in the DGP, so is irrelevant.
- The two regressors are generated as:

$$\begin{pmatrix} x_t \\ z_t \end{pmatrix} \sim \text{MVN} \left[\begin{pmatrix} 0 \\ 0 \end{pmatrix}, \begin{pmatrix} 1 & \rho \\ \rho & 1 \end{pmatrix} \right],$$

  where MVN stands for multivariate normal. Because $\rho = 0$ here, the variance matrix equals the identity matrix, and the two regressors are independently normally distributed (both independent of each other, as well as between successive time periods).

- z is fixed
  This means that the x_t, $t = 1, \ldots, T$ is generated only once, and the same set of observations is used in the 1000 regressions.

5.2.1.2 A 'manual' Monte Carlo

Before we analyze the output, we illustrate the experiment by creating one x_t and four y_ts in GiveWin, and using PcGive to regress the four y_ts on this single x_t. The PcGive output is summarized as:

```
EQ(1)-EQ(4) Modelling Y by OLS
            The estimation sample is: 21 to 80
```

	Coefficient	Std.Error	t-value	Sigma^2
Experiment 1:	1.03856	0.1173	8.85	0.89934
Experiment 2:	1.20762	0.1189	10.2	0.911617
Experiment 3:	0.935901	0.1387	6.75	1.06304
Experiment 4:	0.919268	0.1299	7.08	0.995664

Here, coefficient is the $\widehat{\beta}$, estimated by OLS using (5.1). Std.Error is the estimated standard error (ESE) of the $\widehat{\beta}$, computed as the square root of [see (11.6)]:

$$\widehat{V\left[\widehat{\beta}\right]} = \widehat{\sigma}^2 \left(\sum_{t=1}^{T} x_t^2\right)^{-1}.$$ (5.2)

The t-value is:

$$\frac{\widehat{\beta}}{\left(\widehat{V[\widehat{\beta}]}\right)^{1/2}}.$$

Sigma^2 is the residual variance of the regression:

$$\widehat{\sigma}^2 = \frac{1}{T-1} \sum_{t=1}^{T} \widehat{u}_t \quad \text{where } \widehat{u}_t = y_t - \widehat{\beta} x_t.$$

If x_i denotes the estimated $\widehat{\beta}$ in experiment i, then the mean and standard deviation are:

$$\overline{x} = \frac{1}{M} \sum_{i=1}^{M} x_i \quad \text{and} \quad \sigma_x^2 = \frac{1}{M} \sum_{i=1}^{M} (x_i - \overline{x})^2.$$

So for each column in the regression output above, we can compute these statistics ($M = 4$):

	$\widehat{\beta}$	ESE$[\widehat{\beta}]$	t$_{\beta=0}$	$\widehat{\sigma}^2$
mean	1.0253	0.12620	8.2200	0.96742
std.dev	0.11473	0.0086954	1.3944	0.066501

The square root of σ_x^2 is called the *Monte Carlo standard deviation* or MCSD.

Another aspect worth noting is that there are two measures of the variability in the estimates of $\widehat{\beta}$. The first is the MCSD. The second is the mean of the ESE; ideally these should be close: the ESE should be an accurate estimate of the standard deviation. It is remarkable that with $M = 4$, we already see how well regression can work.

5.2.1.3 Simulation output

The description of the experiment is followed by the results from the simulations:

```
moments of estimates
                    mean            MCSD
Za              0.99543         0.13228
ESE[Za]         0.12845         0.011838
sigma^2         0.99454         0.18273
R^2             0.51069         0.082019
```

```
biases of estimates
                mean bias          MCSE          RMSE      true value
Za            -0.0045741      0.0041832        0.13236         1.0000
ESE[Za]        0.12845        0.00037437       0.12900         0.00000
sigma^2        0.99454        0.0057783        1.0112          0.00000
R^2            0.51069        0.0025937        0.51723         0.00000
```

PcNaive runs 1000 different regressions, a lot more than the four we did by hand, but the output is essentially the same. It starts with the *mean* for Za, which is the mean of the estimated $\widehat{\beta}$. The next column gives the MCSD of $\widehat{\beta}$ from the Monte Carlo experiment.

Because the true value was set to 1.0, and the model corresponds to the DGP, the *mean bias* is $0.9954 - 1.0 = -0.0046$. The variance of the mean bias is σ_x^2/M, and therefore the standard error of the mean bias (the *Monte Carlo standard error* or MCSE) is $M^{-1/2}\sigma_x$, which can be easily checked for the numbers in the output. An approximate 95% confidence interval for the bias is $(-0.0046 - 2 \times 0.004, -0.0046 + 2 \times 0.004)$, so it is not significantly different from zero. This confirms the unbiasedness of the estimate which is shown in (11.3).

Note that the true values for the other coefficients are not really zero, so the reported bias for those is not the actual bias.

Section 11.7 continues the analysis of these results, and subsequent sections report on some additional experiments which are now easily done with PcNaive:

- §11.8 investigates the consequences of making x_t stochastic, i.e. generate a new set in each replication. To achieve this, mark the box labelled Renew Z every replication.

- Perhaps more interesting is the case when the DGP and the model do not coincide. §11.9 looks at the impact of omitted variables. Before you start, can you predict what will happen if the second regressor is erroneously omitted, while being uncorrelated with the first (included) regressor? To implement the experiment in that section with stochastic regressors:

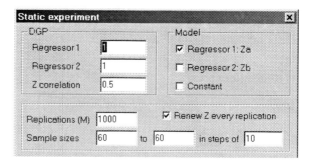

5.2.2 Graphical output from the Static DGP

Rerun the first experiment, marking Data and Histograms under the Plot options:

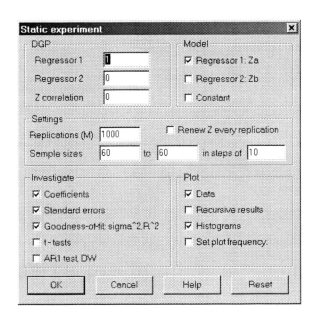

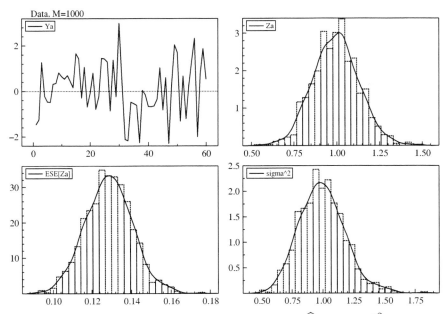

Figure 5.1   Data for final y_t and histogram of $\widehat{\beta}$, ESE and $\widehat{\sigma}^2$.

The graphs are drawn four times, reporting interim results for $M = 250, 500, 750$, and the final results as in Figure 5.1.

The graph shows that the distribution of $\widehat{\beta}$ is close to a normal distribution around the mean of one. The ESE and $\widehat{\sigma}^2$ are slightly skewed, as can be expected, but also appear close to normal otherwise.

Before we close, repeat the second experiment with $\rho = 0.6$, and $\rho = -0.6$, to investigate the impact of omitting a variable which matters and is correlated with an included variable (§11.9 discusses the econometric aspects). Also try including both regressors in the model to see the impact of positive and negative cross-correlation.

The next tutorial will look at the impact of a lagged dependent variable as regressor, and link the results to what can be expected from theory.

Chapter 6

Tutorial for the AR(1) DGP

6.1 Introduction

This chapter walks through the input, simulation output, and the latter's interpretation for the AR(1) DGP. The primary focus of this chapter is on using PcNaive; more theoretical aspects are discussed in Chapter 14 (§§14.3.1,14.3.2,14.4), also see §12.

- The **data generation process** is:

$$y_t = \alpha y_{t-1} + \epsilon_t \text{ with } \epsilon_t \sim \text{IN}\left[0, \sigma_\epsilon^2\right],$$

  where $|\alpha| < 1$, and $t = 0, \ldots, T$.
- The **econometric relationship of interest** is:

$$y_t = \alpha y_{t-1} + u_t \text{ with } u_t \sim \text{IN}\left[0, \sigma^2\right],$$

  which is the same as the DGP.

The objective is understanding the finite sample properties of the OLS estimator $\widehat{\alpha}$ of α, which is:

$$\widehat{\alpha} = \frac{\sum_{t=1}^{T} y_t y_{t-1}}{\sum_{t=1}^{T} y_{t-1}^2}. \tag{6.1}$$

The Monte Carlo **design variables** are $\psi = (\alpha, \sigma_\epsilon^2)'$ and the econometric sample size is T. We consider a single experiment with $(\alpha, \sigma_\epsilon^2) = (0.9, 1.0)$ and $T = 20$. This experimental framework parallels that in Hendry (1984) and is similar to that in Orcutt and Orcutt and Winokur (1969); both of these references will help interpret the results below. Notice that σ is an invariant here as the intercept is zero, and that $|\alpha| < 1$ ensures a stationary process when $y_0 \sim \text{N}[0, \sigma^2/(1 - \alpha^2)]$.

6.2 Designing the AR(1) experiment

We assume that you have already worked your way through the previous tutorials. The same DGP/model editor is used here as in Chapter 4, so formulating the experiment will be straightforward.

41

Start PcNaive, and click on AR(1) DGP. If you continue from the previous chapter, you can press Reset to reset the defaults. Set the starting and ending sample size to 20, the number of replications to 2500, select all options under Investigate, and deactivate all Plot options:

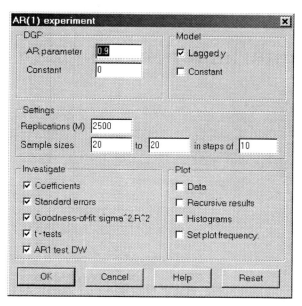

Click on OK, and save this file (as before, a version is already in your PcNaive folder under the name tutar01, so you may wish to use a different name). Then click on Run to do the experiment, which will only take a short while.

6.2.1 Coefficient output from the AR(1) Process

The output commences with a summary of the DGP and model:

```
---- PcNaive (2.00) DGP ----
y is (1 x 1), z is (0 x 1) and fixed.

y[t] = e[t] + A1 y[t-1]
A1 =
     0.90000

e ~ N(0,1)
20 observations discarded

---- System estimation by OLS ----
The available estimation sample is 2 - 21 (T=20)
Ya          lag 0 status Y
Ya          lag 1 status Y
```

Discarding initial observations helps reduce the influence of initial values in stationary processes. For example, after 20 periods, an initial value of y_0 has weight α^{20}, which is 0.12 when $\alpha = 0.9$.

When 20 observations are discarded and the sample size is set to 20, the data are generated for $t = 1, \ldots, 20, 21, \ldots, 41$, and, after discarding the first twenty observations, the generated y_t is based on $t = 21, \ldots, 41$. When the econometric model has y_{t-1} as regressor, an additional observation is lost from the estimation sample, which then is $t = 22, \ldots, 41$, corresponding to $T = 20$. So PcNaive automatically adjust the Monte Carlo sample size to 21, corresponding to a model sample size of 20.

Starting at the bottom of the output, we find the estimate moments and biases:

```
---- PcNaive Monte Carlo results ----
T=21, M=2500, seed=-1 (common)

moments of estimates
                     mean          MCSD
Ya_1              0.83004       0.13752
ESE[Ya_1]         0.11839       0.040011
sigma^2           0.99131       0.32067
R^2               0.74041       0.22514

biases of estimates
                mean bias          MCSE          RMSE      true value
Ya_1            -0.069961     0.0027505       0.15430         0.90000
ESE[Ya_1]        0.11839      0.00080023      0.12496         0.00000
sigma^2          0.99131      0.0064133       1.0419          0.00000
R^2              0.74041      0.0045027       0.77388         0.00000
```

This starts with the *mean* for Ya_1, which is the mean of the estimated $\widehat{\alpha}$ based on (6.1), which has been estimated in each of the M experiments. Because the true value was set to 0.9, and the model corresponds to the DGP, the *mean bias* is approximately $0.83 - 0.9 = -0.07$.

The standard error of the mean bias (the *Monte Carlo standard error* or MCSE) is $M^{-1/2}\sigma_{\widehat{\alpha}} = M^{-1/2}\text{MCSD}$, which can be easily checked for the numbers in the output. With an MCSE of 0.00275, the approximate 95% confidence interval for the bias is $(-0.076, -0.064)$, so it is significantly different from zero.

Asymptotically,

$$T^{1/2}\left(\widehat{\alpha} - \alpha\right) \underset{a}{\sim} \mathsf{N}\left[0, 1 - \alpha^2\right],$$

so $\widehat{\alpha}$ is approximately distributed as $\mathsf{N}[\alpha, (1 - \alpha^2)/T]$ in finite samples. So, least-squares is a consistent estimator for this process and model, implying $\text{plim}(\widehat{\alpha}) = \alpha$. This plim can be calculated numerically in asymptotic analysis. Since the first two moments (at least) exist here, the estimated bias should be approximately zero in large samples. Of course, $T = 20$ is not large, and better analytical approximations to the bias than the asymptote of zero may be available. As shown by Hurwicz (1950), the expectation of $\widehat{\alpha}$ is $(\alpha - 2\alpha/T)$ to $O(T^{-1})$, so the finite-sample bias of $\widehat{\alpha}$ is approximately $-2\alpha/T$, which is -0.09 in this experiment. This works better than zero, but is still outside our simulated confidence interval. A slightly better approximation to $E[\hat{\alpha}]$ in practice, based on a response surface in Hendry (1984) (using a result in Shenton and Johnson, 1965), is $[\alpha - 1.8\alpha/(T+2)]$ which yields a bias of -0.074.

The next entry in the output is entitled ESE[Ya_1], which is the *estimated standard error* of $\hat{\alpha}$, or ESE for short. Because y_{t-1} is the only regressor in the model, it is the square root of diagonal element in $\hat{\sigma}^2(\sum y_{t-1}^2)^{-1}$. Since $E[\hat{\sigma}^2] = 1$, $E[X'X] = T/(1-\alpha^2)$, and $\hat{\sigma}^2$ and $(X'X)$ are approximately uncorrelated, the mean of the ESE is approximately $[(1-\alpha^2)/T]^{1/2} = 0.097$, which here is also the approximate standard error of the estimator. Whilst the estimated mean of the ESE is numerically reasonably close to 0.097, it is statistically significantly different from it, noting that the standard error of the estimated mean of the ESE is $0.0008 = 0.04/\sqrt{2500}$. However, the mean ESE is close to the MCSD (reported above as 0.13752). The asymptotic approximation becomes increasingly poor as α gets closer to unity.

The R^2 is defined as:

$$R^2 = \frac{ESS}{RSS} = \frac{\sum(\hat{y}_t - \bar{y})^2}{\sum(y_t - \bar{y})^2}. \qquad (6.2)$$

When the regression has a constant term:

$$R^2 = 1 - \frac{RSS}{TSS} = 1 - \frac{\sum\hat{\epsilon}_t^2}{\sum(y_t - \bar{y})^2}. \qquad (6.3)$$

When there is a constant term the residuals have zero mean, and (6.2) and (6.3) will give identical answers. PcNaive uses (6.2) in its computations.

Despite the fact that the current model does not have a constant term, we continue from (6.3):

$$E\left[R^2\right] \approx 1 - \frac{E\left[\epsilon_t^2\right]}{E\left[y_t^2\right] - 0} = \alpha^2.$$

For this experiment, $\alpha^2 = 0.81$. The residual sum of squares, RSS, is approximately distributed as a $\chi^2(T-1)$. That implies an approximate mean and standard deviation of $(T-1)$ and $[2(T-1)]^{1/2}$, which are 19 and 6.2 for $T = 20$. That also implies that $\hat{\sigma}^2$ has an approximate mean and standard deviation of 1.00 and 0.32 respectively. All the outcomes from the simulation are again close to their approximate theoretical values; R^2 is somewhat of an exception, because our analysis assumed that a constant was present in the regression.

6.2.2 Test output from the AR(1) Process

The remaining output concerns the test statistics which were simulated:

```
moments of test statistics
                        mean        std.dev      skewness   ex.kurtosis
t-Ya_1                8.2611         4.0154        0.97489       1.2253
AR1                   0.96472        1.4073        2.9454       12.210
DW                    1.8644         0.36011       0.060635     -0.11300

critical values (tail quantiles)
                  5%
AR1             3.7021
DW              2.4675

critical values (two sided: left tail quantiles)
                    2.5%
t-Ya_1            2.3682

critical values (two sided: right tail quantiles)
                    2.5%
t-Ya_1           18.188

rejection frequencies
                    5%
t-Ya_1           0.98320
AR1              0.034000
DW               0.021600
[ASE]            0.0043589
```

This table starts with the first four moments (mean, standard deviation, skewness and excess kurtosis, i.e. kurtosis-3) of the t-statistic on $\hat{\alpha}$. At the bottom is the percentage rejection frequency at the nominal % critical values. Two types of t-statistics could be examined, one for testing $\alpha = 0$ and the other for testing $\alpha = \alpha_0$ where α_0 is the true value ($\alpha_0 = 0.9$ here). Only the former is reported in the output above.

Noting that $E[\hat{\alpha}] \approx 0.84$ and that $E[ESE] \approx 0.097$, we have:

$$E[t(\alpha = 0)] = E[\hat{\alpha}/ESE] \approx E[\hat{\alpha}]/E[ESE] = 8.7.$$

This is the (approximate) non-centrality of $t(\alpha = 0)$ and implies a very high (virtually 100%) rejection frequency.

The second statistic, $t(\alpha = 0.9)$, is approximately distributed as a central t-statistic with 19 degrees of freedom, and so has a standard deviation of essentially unity and a rejection frequency of approximately 5%. To simulate this, rerun the experiment with $\alpha = 0$ in the DGP. The outcomes match these theoretical results, finding a rejection frequency of 3%. Note that the rejection frequency for an underlying rejection rate p, has a standard error of $ASE = (p[1 - p]/M)^{1/2}$. The following table gives the standard errors for various values of p and m:

	p = 0.1	p = 0.05	p = 0.01	p = 0.001
$M = 100$	0.0300	0.0218	0.00995	0.00316
$M = 200$	0.0212	0.0154	0.00704	0.00223
$M = 1000$	0.00949	0.00689	0.00315	0.000999
$M = 2500$	0.00600	0.00436	0.00199	0.000632
$M = 10\,000$	0.00300	0.00218	0.000995	0.000316

This is reported as [ASE] in the output; in the current situation, the standard error is 0.436%, so 3% is significantly low.

The next statistic is the Durbin–Watson, defined as:

$$DW = \frac{\sum_{t=2}^{T} \left(\widehat{\epsilon}_t - \widehat{\epsilon}_{t-1}\right)^2}{\sum_{t=1}^{T} \widehat{\epsilon}_t^2}. \tag{6.4}$$

DW is most powerful as a test of $\{\epsilon_t\}$ being white noise against:

$$\epsilon_t = \rho\epsilon_{t-1} + \nu_t \text{ where } \nu_t \sim \text{IID}\left(0, \sigma_\nu^2\right).$$

Two critical values for the Durbin-Watson statistic could be considered, one for the standard test that $\rho = 0$ and the other for the unit-root test that $\rho = 1$. Only the former is listed. As shown in (e.g.) Phillips and Wickens (1978, pp. 200–212):

$$T^{1/2}\left(DW - 2\right) \xrightarrow{D} \text{N}[0, 4]$$

under the null hypothesis of white-noise disturbances, so in finite samples, DW is approximately distributed N[2, $4/T$]. That result implies a mean and standard deviation of 2.0 and 0.2 in this experiment. The critical values used by PcNaive are based on the asymptotic distribution, implying 'asymptotic' rejection frequencies of 5%.

Even though the Durbin–Watson test for $\rho = 0$ happens to have rejected 2.2% of the time, DW is not consistent for this model because of the lagged dependent variable (this will be more noticeable when additional regressors are included), and the critical value is inappropriate since no constant is included in the regression!

The AR1 test, on the other hand, is (asymptotically) valid here. It is the test on lagged residuals in an auxiliary regression, which is approximately F(1, $T - k - 1$)-distributed. More details can be found in Hendry and Doornik (2001), as well as Breusch (1978), Godfrey (1978), Kiviet (1986) and Doornik (1996). Notice that the theoretical mean should be around 1.1 with a standard deviation of about 1.75 and a skewness of 3.85 (see Johnson, Kotz and Balakrishnan, 1995, p.326).

6.3 Recursive Monte Carlo

To finish this chapter, we can graphically verify that the bias appears with sample size. So adjust the initial experiment of this chapter by setting the sample size from 20 to

120 in steps of 10, and selecting Recursive plots. Figure 6.1a shows that the bias does indeed get smaller. The residual variance appears to be unbiased at all sample sizes (Fig. 6.1c).

The final two graphs show that the DW remains biased (its problems were discussed above), but that the AR(1) test is well behaved (by default, the rejection frequencies are plotted on $[0, 1]$, but in the graph we changed that to show the results more precisely).

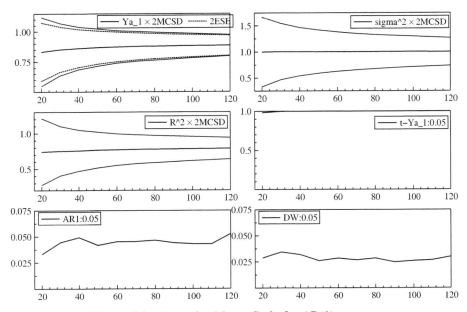

Figure 6.1   Recursive Monte Carlo for AR(1) process.

Chapter 7

Tutorial on the PcNaive DGP

7.1 Introduction

The PcNaive DGP allows for much more general experiments than those considered hitherto. The full specification is given in (2.3), but in its default format, which has one y equation, and no z, it is not that dissimilar to the AR(1) DGP:

$$
\begin{aligned}
\mathbf{y}_t &= \mathbf{A}_1 \mathbf{y}_{t-1} + \mathbf{a}_3 + \mathbf{e}_t, \\
\mathbf{e}_t &\sim \mathrm{MVN}\left[\mathbf{0}, \mathbf{I}_n\right], \\
\mathbf{z}_t &= \mathbf{0}.
\end{aligned}
$$

In general $\mathbf{y}_t$ is an n-vector, and $\mathbf{z}_t$ a q-vector; here $n = 1$, $q = 0$. The ys are labelled Ya, Yb, ..., and the zs Za, Zb, ... The distribution of the error term in the y equation can be changed from the default standard normal.

7.2 Example 1: AR(1) process

To start simply, we mimic the Monte Carlo experiment for the AR(1) process of the previous tutorial. Designing the experiment involves several steps:

(1) General
    To set the dimensions of y and z and add various extensions to the basic DGP.
(2) Y DGP
    To set the coefficients for the y DGP.

48

(3) Z DGP

To set the coefficients for the z DGP (if any z are used).

(4) Errors

To set the parameters for the error distributions.

(5) Model

To formulate the econometric model.

(6) Stats

To determine which coefficients and tests to report, and which graphs to make.

(7) Settings

To set Monte Carlo parameters such as the number of replications (M) and the sample size.

We shall consider each page in turn, although in most cases the default will suffice.

7.2.1 General **page**

The general page defaults to $n = 1$ and $q = 0$:

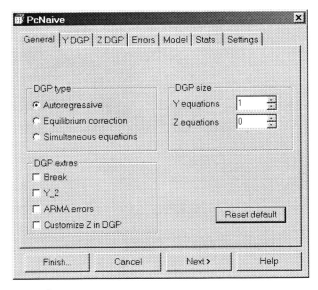

Press Next to turn to the next page.

7.2.2 Y DGP **page**

Here we must set the autoregressive parameter to 0.9. The column on the left switches between the different coefficient matrices. The $\mathbf{A}_1$ matrix is already selected. Click on the value zero in the matrix, and change it to 0.9:

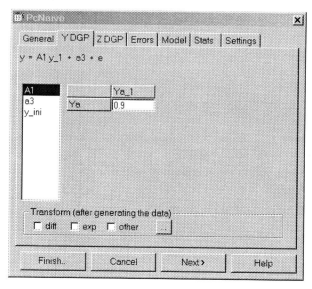

Press Next to turn to the next page.

7.2.3 Z DGP **page**

There are no z variables:

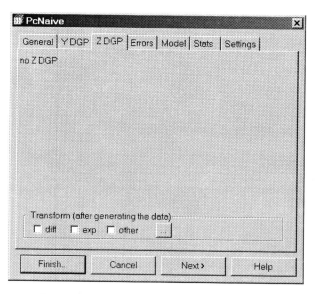

Press Next to turn to the next page.

7.2.4 Errors **page**

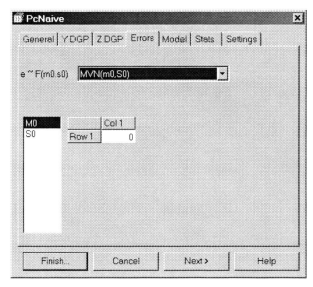

Keep the default of standard normal (because $n = 1$, the multivariate normal distribution, MVN, coincides with the univariate normal), so press Next to turn to the next page.

7.2.5 Model **page**

Model formulation is identical to that used in PcGive. The content of the 'database' is determined by the choices made up to this point.

Our model is just a regression on the lagged dependent variable. So, delete the Constant from the model (select it with the mouse, and then click on Delete or press the Del key). To add y_{t-1}, select *Ya* in the database, and press Add. This will add Ya_1 provided that the lag length is set to one (with the radio button in front of it selected).

There are various alternatives, including:

- Double click on *Ya*.
- Set lag length to Query, and repeat the previous actions. Now you are prompted to specify a lag length.

The status of a variable can be changed by selecting it in the model, and then clicking one of the status buttons. Here *Ya* is marked as endogenous. When a variable has no status, it is a normal regressor (or Z variable, but unrelated to the status in the DGP: you may add a variable which is a y_t in the DGP as a regressor in the model). Unrestricted only matters for cointegration analysis, and additional instruments for IV estimation.

The final model should be:

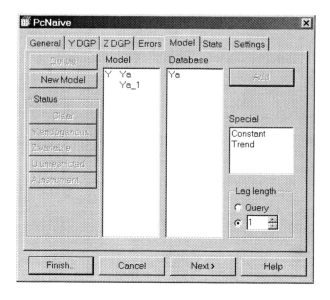

7.2.6 Stats **page**

The lists on the right of the Stats page give the available statistics and plots. The desired entries should be moved to the lists on the left. This can be done by double clicking on an entry, or selecting and pressing <<. The reverse action will remove. Double click on Rec. coefficients in the Plots to create list at the bottom left to remove it, giving the desired choice:

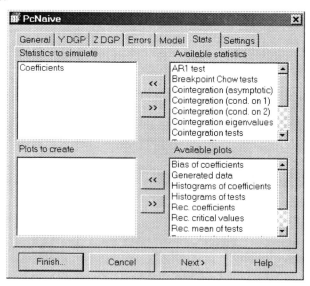

Press Next to turn to the next page.

7.2.7 Settings **page**

We arrive at the settings page in which a range of control parameters can be changed. Set $M = 2500$ and a sample size from 20 to 20.

This dialog does not know the true parameter values, and we can help PcNaive by entering the values under True parameters. It expects a comma-separated list, but here there is only one value:

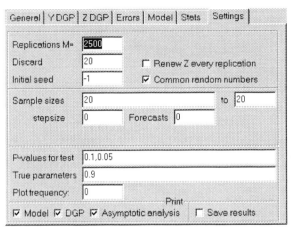

7.2.8 Saving and running the experiment

Finally, we can save the experiment by clicking on Finish, specifying a disk file name, and then run it in the standard way by clicking on Run in the main dialog.

7.2.9 Output from the experiment

The output is the same as before, with the addition of asymptotic analysis (see Ch. 16):

```
Companion matrix:
Ya          0.9          0
Ya_1         1           0

Variance matrix of companion form:
Ya           1           0
Ya_1         0           0

eigenvalues of companion matrix:
      real       imag    modulus
         0          0          0
       0.9          0        0.9
The DGP is stationary.

Long-run mean of y_t:
          Ya
```

```
        0.00000
M matrix
          Ya              Ya_1
        5.2632          4.7368
        4.7368          5.2632
Plims for OLS estimates of linear model, T=20:
                        Ya_1
beta                  0.90000
SE[beta]              0.097468
sigma^2 = 1

Long-run matrix Pi(1)-I = Po:
      -0.10000
rank of long-run matrix: 1
Mean-lag matrix sum pi_i:
       0.90000
This DGP is I(0).
```

Asymptotically, $T^{\frac{1}{2}}(\widehat{\alpha}-\alpha)$ is distributed as $N[0, 1-\alpha^2]$ (see §6.2.1), so $\widehat{\alpha}$ is approximately distributed as $N[\alpha, (1-\alpha^2)/T]$ in finite samples. Under the header `Plims for linear model, T=20` we find `beta` which is the *plim*$(\widehat{\alpha})$ for this model. It equals α, which is 0.90, because the estimator is consistent. The `SE[beta]` is $\sqrt{[(1-\alpha^2)/T]}$, which is 0.097.

So, when possible, PcNaive gives the theoretical as well as the simulated answer!

7.3 Example 2: unit roots

7.3.1 DF and ADF tests for unit roots

PcNaive allows easy study of Dickey–Fuller and Augmented Dickey–Fuller tests recursively, and the motivation for this sub-section is to explain how to do so as an indication of a general feature of the program. Consider the issue of testing an individual marginal process $\{y_t\}$ for a unit root using the Dickey–Fuller test. This involves rewriting:

$$y_t = \beta y_{t-1} + u_t,$$

as a regression of Δy_t on y_{t-1}:

$$\Delta y_t = \delta y_{t-1} + u_t, \tag{7.1}$$

and testing the null $H_0 : \delta = 0$ (which corresponds to $H_0 : \beta = 1$), using a t-test but with appropriate critical values (see MacKinnon, 1991, for response surface approximations from which accurate critical values can be obtained). The augmented DF test (ADF) adds lagged Δy_{t-i} to (7.1).

7.3.2 Experiments with unit roots

The objective here is not to provide a detailed discussion of the econometrics, but to show how PcNaive can be used to analyze the problem. Sections 12.8 and 12.9 provide more information (for a recent survey see Phillips and Xiao, 1998). Further examples which use PcNaive for unit-root analysis are in Banerjee, Dolado, Galbraith and Hendry (1993) and Hendry (1995a).

Implementing the model as (7.1) requires the PcNaive DGP, so select that option, and click on Reset to set all options back to the default. In the Y DGP set the autoregressive parameter to unity, and click on diff:

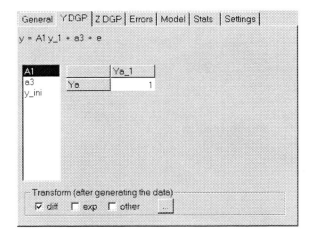

This will add the Δy_t to the model database, as can be seen on the Model page:

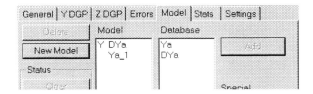

Formulate the model (7.1) as shown above. The interest is in the estimated coefficients and their t-values, so select those. For plots, select the histograms and generated data:

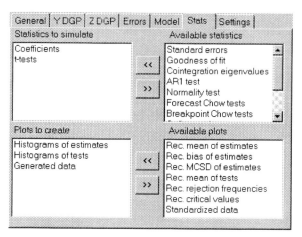

Finally, we used $M = 10\,000$, $T = 50$, and zero discarded initial observations to ensure $y_0 = 0$. To make the experiments more lively, we set the plot frequency to 1000, so that the plots will be updated 10 times during the experiment:

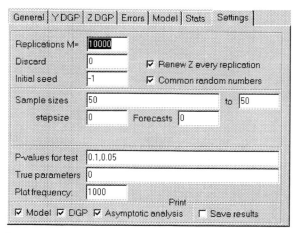

Despite the large number of replications, this experiment `tutpcnaive02a` only took 5 seconds on our computer. The resulting final graph is in Figure 7.1. Notice the skewness of the distribution of $\widehat{\delta} = \widehat{\beta} - 1$, as well as for the distribution of the t-value. However, the Monte Carlo critical values are not that far removed from the $t(49)$ values of 1.7 and 2.0:

```
---- PcNaive Monte Carlo results ----
T=51, M=10000, seed=-1 (common)

moments of test statistics
                    mean      std.dev      skewness    ex.kurtosis
t-Ya_1          -0.41109      0.98318       0.29478        0.26568

critical values (two sided: left tail quantiles)
```

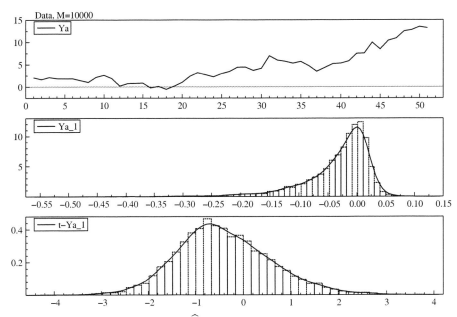

Figure 7.1 Distribution of $\widehat{\beta} - 1$ and its t-value in a unit-root model.

```
                       5%           2.5%
t-Ya_1              -1.9031       -2.2138

critical values (two sided: right tail quantiles)
                       5%           2.5%
t-Ya_1               1.3166        1.6765

rejection frequencies
                      10%            5%
t-Ya_1             0.10890       0.051500
[ASE]             0.0030000      0.0021794
```

If we do not consider the explosive alternative as relevant, the interest is in a one sided test, where the null is a unit root ($\delta = 0$), against the alternative of a stationary process ($\delta < 0$, i.e. $\beta < 1$; Nielsen, 2001, discusses the impact of unstable roots).

Unlike the stationary case, the addition of a constant term to the model has quite an impact, see Figure 7.2. The distribution of the t-value is still skewed, but also very much shifted to the left. The Monte Carlo reports a 5% left-sided critical value of -2.9. The conventional critical value rejects the null of a unit root 28% of the time, which is much too often.

PcNaive has the ADF test built in. To use it, the model must be formulated in levels:

```
Model            Database
Y Ya             Ya
U Constant       DYa
   Ya_1
```

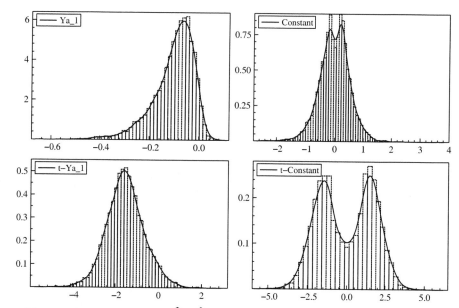

Figure 7.2   Distribution of $\widehat{\beta}_0$, $\widehat{\beta}_1 - 1$ and their t-values in a unit-root model.

Then select Co/integration tests from the available statistics, removing the t-values. The 5% rejection frequencies are now not significantly different from 5%:

```
                  10%           5%
ADF(0;c)       0.050600      0.050600
[ASE]          0.0030000     0.0021794
```

Note that the 10% values are not what they seem. PcNaive only has critical values for the ADF test, not the whole distribution (and hence no p-values). The routine returns one if the test statistic is less than the 5% critical value, and zero otherwise. Therefore, only the five percent values can be used.

7.3.3 Single equation model with cointegration

Consider the DGP of Banerjee, Dolado, Galbraith and Hendry (1993, p.221):

$$\begin{array}{llll} y_t & = & \gamma_1 y_{t-1} + \gamma_2 x_t + \gamma_3 x_{t-1} + \epsilon_{1t}, & \epsilon_{1t} \sim \mathrm{N}[0, \sigma_1^2], \\ \Delta x_t & = & \epsilon_{2t}, & \epsilon_{2t} \sim \mathrm{N}[0, \sigma_2^2], \end{array} \quad (7.2)$$

with long-run homogeneity: $\gamma_1 + \gamma_2 + \gamma_3 = 1$. The first equation can then be written as:

$$\Delta y_t = \gamma_2 \Delta x_t + (\gamma_1 - 1)(y_{t-1} - x_{t-1}) + \epsilon_{1t}. \quad (7.3)$$

To set up this DGP, select Simultaneous equations with two Y equations on the general page, then use *Ya* for y_t, and *Yb* for x_t, and take $\gamma_1 = 0.9$, $\gamma_2 = 0.5$. So enter the coefficient matrices as:

$$\mathbf{A}_0 = \begin{pmatrix} 0 & 0.5 \\ 0 & 0 \end{pmatrix}, \quad \mathbf{A}_1 = \begin{pmatrix} 0.9 & -0.4 \\ 0 & 1 \end{pmatrix}.$$

Formulate the model analogous to the first equation of (7.2) making Yb_t exogenous, with the addition of a constant term. Select the statistics as:

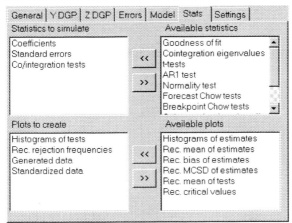

We can mimic Banerjee, Dolado, Galbraith and Hendry (1993) in the choice of sample sizes: $T = 25, 50, 100, 200, 400$. Instead of using the step size, just enter the comma separated list:

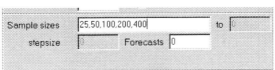

The reported cointegration test is the ECM test, see §12.10. Because the null of no cointegration (analogous to the null of non-stationarity in the ADF test) is false, the rejection frequency goes to one. As with the ADF test, only 5% critical values are used. As Figure 7.3 shows, the power to detect the cointegration at sample sizes less than 100 is still fairly low (we used $M = 1000$).

7.3.4 Cointegration analysis

From here, it is a small step to add tests for cointegration analysis based on the Johansen procedure. We do not wish to enter into detail here (see §13.7 and the references therein). The only required change is to mark Yb in the model as an endogenous variable. PcNaive will then automatically do the vector autoregressive version of the cointegration test. Although most commonly we estimate the cointegration analysis with an unrestricted constant and restricted trend (see §2.3.4 and Doornik and Hendry, 2001b), we adopted a restricted constant here. Figure 7.4c shows that the power to

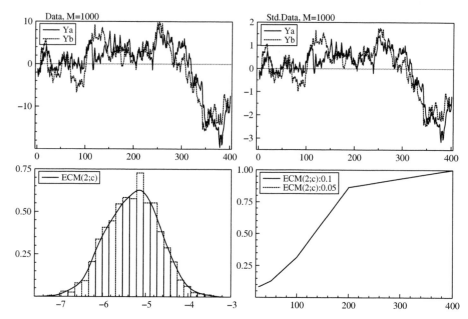

Figure 7.3 Cointegrated process: data, standardized data, distribution of ECM test and rejection frequencies.

reject zero unit roots goes towards unity, while the size of rejecting one cointegrating vector in favour of two is well behaved.

7.3.5 DGP in equilibrium correction form

An alternative method for parametrizing the DGP is to enter it in error-correction (or more accurately: equilibrium-correction) form. This specifies the cointegrating rank directly. The starting point is (7.3), but we must remove the simultaneity from:

$$\begin{pmatrix} 1 & -\gamma_2 \\ 0 & 1 \end{pmatrix}\begin{pmatrix} \Delta y_t \\ \Delta x_t \end{pmatrix} = \begin{pmatrix} \gamma_1 - 1 \\ 0 \end{pmatrix}\begin{pmatrix} 1 & -1 \end{pmatrix}\begin{pmatrix} y_{t-1} \\ x_{t-1} \end{pmatrix} + \begin{pmatrix} \epsilon_{1,t} \\ \epsilon_{2,t} \end{pmatrix}.$$

Therefore, pre-multiply the system by:

$$\mathbf{D}^{-1} = \begin{pmatrix} 1 & -\gamma_2 \\ 0 & 1 \end{pmatrix}^{-1} = \begin{pmatrix} 1 & \gamma_2 \\ 0 & 1 \end{pmatrix},$$

which gives:

$$\begin{pmatrix} \Delta y_t \\ \Delta x_t \end{pmatrix} = \begin{pmatrix} \gamma_1 - 1 \\ 0 \end{pmatrix}\begin{pmatrix} 1 & -1 \end{pmatrix}\begin{pmatrix} y_{t-1} \\ x_{t-1} \end{pmatrix} + \begin{pmatrix} \nu_{1,t} \\ \nu_{2,t} \end{pmatrix}, \quad \nu \sim \mathsf{N}[\mathbf{0}, \mathbf{D}^{-1}\mathbf{D}^{-1\prime}].$$

These computations are done for you in the asymptotic analysis.

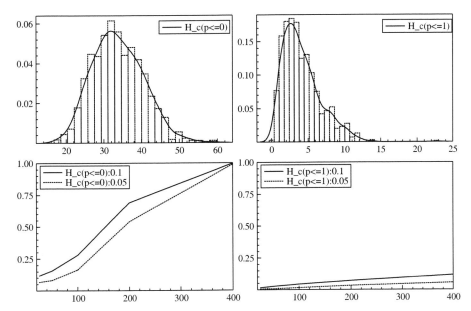

Figure 7.4 Cointegrated process: distribution and rejection frequencies of cointegration tests.

Select Equilibrium correction on the General page, with Rank long run equal to one:

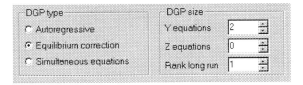

The DGP is written as:

$$\Delta \mathbf{y}_t = \alpha \beta' \mathbf{y}_{t-1} + \mathbf{a}_3 + \mathbf{e}_t,$$

where α and β are $n \times p$ matrices when p is the rank of the long-run matrix (the number of cointegrating vectors). If you follow on from before, the coefficient matrices are already filled in correctly:

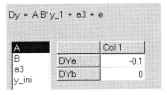

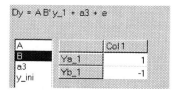

with the exception of the residual variance matrix, which now is:[1]

$$\mathbf{S}_0 = \begin{pmatrix} 1 + \gamma_2^2 & \gamma_2 \\ \gamma_2 & 1 \end{pmatrix}.$$

7.4 Example 3: autoregressive error and asymptotic analysis

We implement the DGP of Chapter 16, consisting of a bivariate simultaneous equations model with first-order autoregressive error of -0.6. The equation of interest links Ya_t to Yb_t and Ya_{t-1} with coefficients 0.5 and 0.5 respectively. The equation determining Yb_t is a partial adjustment to Za_t, with coefficients of 0.8 and 1.0, where Za_t is simply an autoregression with coefficient 0.75. All of the error variances are unity, and all covariances 0.2; all intercepts are also zero:

$$\begin{pmatrix} Ya \\ Yb \end{pmatrix}_t = \begin{pmatrix} 0 & 0.5 \\ 0 & 0 \end{pmatrix} \begin{pmatrix} Ya \\ Yb \end{pmatrix}_t + \begin{pmatrix} 0.5 & 0 \\ 0 & 0.8 \end{pmatrix} \begin{pmatrix} Ya \\ Yb \end{pmatrix}_{t-1} + \begin{pmatrix} 0 \\ 1 \end{pmatrix} Za_t + \mathbf{u}_t,$$

$$\begin{pmatrix} Ua \\ Ub \end{pmatrix}_t = \mathbf{u}_t = \begin{pmatrix} -0.6 & 0 \\ 0 & 0 \end{pmatrix} \begin{pmatrix} Ua \\ Ub \end{pmatrix}_{t-1} + \mathbf{e}_t, \tag{7.4}$$

$$\mathbf{e}_t \sim \text{IN} \left[\mathbf{0}, \begin{pmatrix} 1 & 0.2 \\ 0.2 & 1 \end{pmatrix} \right],$$

$$Za_t = 0.75 Za_{t-1} + \mathbf{v}_t, \quad \mathbf{v}_t \sim \text{IN}[0,1].$$

Select PcNaive DGP from the main dialog, starting at the General page. If you continue from the previous exercise, press the Reset default button first. Set the DGP type to simultaneous equations, the number of Y and Z equations to two and one respectively. Mark ARMA errors under DGP extras:

---

[1]The results of the two implementations are close, but not identical. The reason is that the reduced-form residuals are generated differently. In the simultaneous equations model, they are $\mathbf{D}^{-1}\boldsymbol{\epsilon}_t$. However, in the equilibrium correction form, when $\mathbf{S}_0 = \mathbf{D}^{-1}\mathbf{D}^{-1\prime}$, they are generated as $\mathbf{P}\boldsymbol{\epsilon}_t$, where $\mathbf{P}$ is the Choleski decomposition of $\mathbf{S}_0$:

$$\mathbf{P} = \begin{pmatrix} (1+\gamma_2^2)^{1/2} & \gamma_2(1+\gamma_2^2)^{-1/2} \\ 0 & (1+\gamma_2^2)^{-1/2} \end{pmatrix}.$$

So the reduced-form errors have the same distribution, but are numerically different.

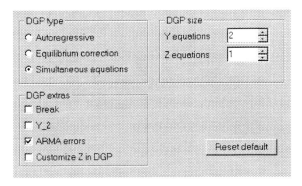

The Y DGP now has the form:

$$\mathbf{y}_t = \mathbf{A}_0\mathbf{y}_t + \mathbf{A}_1\mathbf{y}_{t-1} + \mathbf{A}_2\mathbf{z}_t + \mathbf{a}_3 + \mathbf{u}_t,$$

and the coefficient matrices have to be entered one at a time:

A0		Ya	Yb
A1	Ya	0	0.5
A2	Yb	0	0
a3			
y_ini			

A0		Ya_1	Yb_1
A1	Ya	0.5	0
A2	Yb	0	0.8
a3			
y_ini			

A0		Za
A1	Ya	0
A2	Yb	1
a3		
y_ini		

Press Next to go to the Z DGP page; this has the form:

$$\mathbf{z}_t = \mathbf{C}_0\mathbf{z}_{t-1} + \mathbf{c}_1 + \mathbf{c}_2t + \mathbf{v}_t.$$

Set the autoregressive parameter to 0.75, leaving the rest at zero:

z = C0 z_1 + c1 + c2 t + v

C0		Za_1
c1	Za	0.75
c2		
z_ini		

Next again goes to the Error page:

$$\mathbf{u}_t \;=\; \mathbf{B}_0\mathbf{u}_{t-1} + \mathbf{e}_t + \mathbf{B}_1\mathbf{e}_{t-1},$$
$$\mathbf{e}_t \;\sim\; \ldots,$$
$$\mathbf{v}_t \;\sim\; \ldots.$$

Both e_t and v_t already have a standard normal distribution, which is fine. Enter $\mathbf{B}_0$:

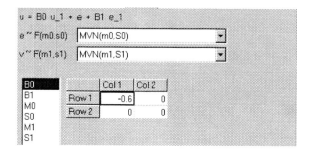

and then $\mathbf{S}_0$:

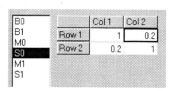

Turning to the Model page, we will estimate a linear single-equation model, regressing Ya_t on $(Yb_t : Ya_{t-1})$, by OLS. Thus, the autoregressive error is left untreated. Formulate this model (ensure that Yb_t is not entered as Y variable, which would result in a two-equation model; to clear its status, double click on it, or select and press Clear):

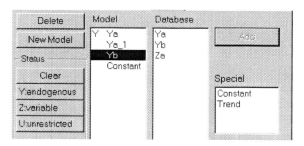

Note that PcNaive will reorder the model to put lagged dependent variables first, and unrestricted variables last. This is relevant when the true parameter values are entered below.

Specify the statistics to simulate as follows:

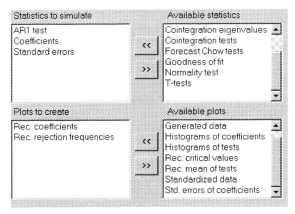

Finally, in the last page, set the number of replications to 1000, ensure that Z is renewed at every replication, set the sample size from 60 to 120 in steps of 20, and the true parameters to 0.5, 0.5:

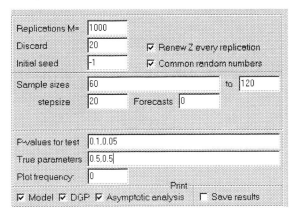

Figure 7.5 shows the substantial bias caused by the untreated autoregressive error, although the MCSD and ESE show close correspondence. The test for autoregressive errors has very high power to detect this, fortunately, even at 0.01 and $T = 60$, it rejects essentially 100% of the time.

The output of the asymptotic analysis includes the plims of this model:

```
Long-run mean of y_t:
          Ya              Yb
     0.00000         0.00000
M matrix
       Ya          Yb         Ya_1        Yb_1        Ya_2        Yb_2          Za
    27.104      26.561      25.138      26.612      24.177      25.692      4.5714
    26.561      28.175      24.678      26.825      22.313      24.675      5.7143
    25.138      24.678      27.104      26.561      25.138      26.612      3.4286
    26.612      26.825      26.561      28.175      24.678      26.825      4.2857
    24.177      22.313      25.138      24.678      27.104      26.561      2.5714
    25.692      24.675      26.612      26.825      26.561      28.175      3.2143
```

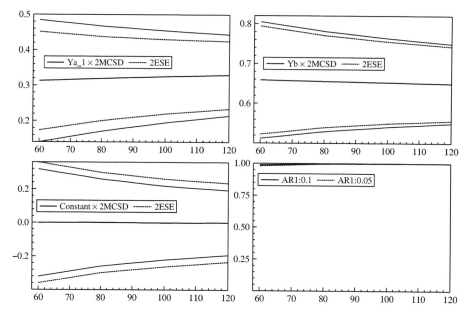

Figure 7.5   Bias in simultaneous model with untreated autocorrelated errors.

```
     4.5714     5.7143     3.4286     4.2857     2.5714     3.2143     2.2857

Plims for linear model, T=120:
                       Ya_1                Yb
beta                0.34138           0.64373
SE[beta]            0.046492          0.045599
sigma^2 = 1.42374
```

This is precisely the illustration that is used in Chapter 16, and the results here are identical to the calculations in that chapter. Note how close the plims are to the mean estimated coefficients.

Because this is a simultaneous equations model ($A_0 \neq 0$), the output also includes the reduced form:

$$\mathbf{y}_t = \begin{pmatrix} 0.5 & 0.4 \\ 0 & 0.8 \end{pmatrix} \mathbf{y}_{t-1} + \begin{pmatrix} 0.5 \\ 1 \end{pmatrix} \mathbf{z}_t + \mathbf{w}_t,$$

which is obtained by premultiplying the $\mathbf{y}_t$ equation by $\mathbf{D}^{-1} = (\mathbf{I}_n - \mathbf{A}_0)^{-1}$. The error term then becomes:

$$\mathbf{w}_t \equiv \mathbf{D}^{-1}\mathbf{u}_t = \mathbf{D}^{-1}\mathbf{B}_0\mathbf{u}_{t-1} + \mathbf{e}_t^*,$$

where

$$\mathbf{e}_t^* \sim \mathsf{MVN}\left[\mathbf{0}, \mathbf{D}^{-1}\mathbf{S}_0\mathbf{D}^{-1\prime}\right] = \mathsf{MVN}\left[\mathbf{0}, \begin{pmatrix} 1.45 & 0.7 \\ 0.7 & 1 \end{pmatrix}\right].$$

This variance is listed in the output as $V[w]$.

7.5 Example 4: simultaneity and inter-estimator comparison

It is possible to remove the common factor restriction which is implicit in model (7.4). Using L for the lag operator ($Lx_t = x_{t-1}$) we can rewrite the $\mathbf{u}_t$ equation as:

$$\begin{pmatrix} 1 + 0.6L & 0 \\ 0 & 1 \end{pmatrix} \mathbf{u}_t = \mathbf{e}_t.$$

Therefore, premultiplying $\mathbf{y}_t$ in (7.4) by:

$$\begin{pmatrix} 1 + 0.6L & 0 \\ 0 & 1 \end{pmatrix}$$

removes the autocorrelation:

$$\mathbf{y}_t = \begin{pmatrix} 0 & 0.5 \\ 0 & 0 \end{pmatrix} \mathbf{y}_t + \begin{pmatrix} 0.5 & 0.3 \\ 0 & 0.8 \end{pmatrix} \mathbf{y}_{t-1} + \begin{pmatrix} 0.3 & 0 \\ 0 & 0 \end{pmatrix} \mathbf{y}_{t-2} + \begin{pmatrix} 0 \\ 1 \end{pmatrix} \mathbf{z}_t + \mathbf{e}_t.$$

The only adjustment required in the previous experiment is to add Yb_{t-1} and Ya_{t-2} to the estimated model. The results in Figure 7.6 shows that the bias is still there: the estimated mean coefficient on Yb_t is 0.584. This time it is caused by neglected simultaneity: Yb_t is an endogenous variable. Note that the test for autocorrelated residuals is now well behaved.[2] The asymptotic analysis confirms the Monte Carlo output:

```
Plims for linear model, T=120:
                       Ya_1            Ya_2              Yb            Yb_1
beta               -0.087553         0.31409         0.58515         0.19485
SE[beta]            0.076341         0.047522        0.059056        0.095593
sigma^2 = 0.982969
Monte Carlo simulations
mean               -0.091658         0.30603         0.58446         0.20654
mean SE             0.078732         0.049164        0.060991        0.098486
```

Once again, asymptotic and finite-sample outcomes are close for both estimates and standard errors: the asymptotic calculations allow for the unmodelled simultaneity here.

To remove the bias, we can estimate by IV, noting that Za_t is a valid instrument for Yb_t (also see §16.5.3). To implement IV, mark Yb as endogenous in the model, add the current values of Za, and mark them as additional instrument:

---

[2]In general, it is dangerous to accept the alternative hypothesis when a mis-specification test rejects, as there can be other causes for a significant test outcome.

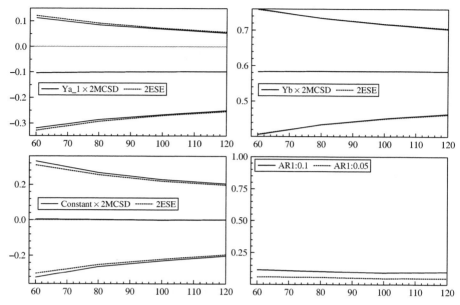

Figure 7.6   Simultaneity bias.

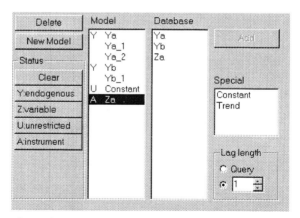

The result confirms that IV estimation removes the simultaneity bias:

```
moments of estimates  mean              MCSD
Yb                     0.49662          0.080492
Ya_1                  -0.11284          0.078354
Ya_2                   0.29459          0.050443
Yb_1                   0.31929          0.11849
Constant               0.0020536        0.10679
ESE[Yb]                0.081680         0.010476
ESE[Ya_1]              0.079380         0.0049017
ESE[Ya_2]              0.050264         0.0040064
ESE[Yb_1]              0.11905          0.013434
ESE[Constant]          0.10014          0.014142
```

Notice that by using common random numbers both OLS and IV are applied to the same set of artificial data. This trick minimizes the variance of the inter-estimator differences.

Another way to obtain unbiased estimates is to estimate the model simultaneously. Clear the status of Za in the previous model:

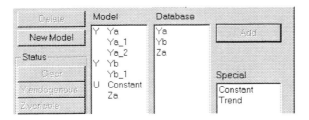

In this case, PcNaive will automatically estimate the model by multivariate OLS. The results for the unrestricted reduced form are: first, for the asymptotic analysis:

```
Plims for linear model, T=120:beta
                Ya              Yb
Ya_1       -0.10000               0
Ya_2        0.30000               0
Yb_1        0.70000         0.80000
Za          0.50000          1.0000
SE[beta]
                Ya              Yb
Ya_1       0.093158        0.077364
Ya_2       0.058616        0.048678
Yb_1       0.085609        0.071094
Za         0.094653        0.078605
sigma^2
         1.4500         0.70000
        0.70000          1.0000
```

and then for the Monte Carlo result (only listing the results for the first equation):

```
moments of estimates
                     mean            MCSD
Ya_1@Ya           -0.11319        0.094623
Ya_2@Ya            0.29449        0.061747
Yb_1@Ya            0.71508        0.089128
Za@Ya              0.50083        0.095207
Constant@Ya       0.0013872        0.12804
ESE[Ya_1@Ya]       0.094803       0.0070744
ESE[Ya_2@Ya]       0.060017       0.0042466
ESE[Yb_1@Ya]       0.087848       0.0077762
ESE[Za@Ya]         0.097909       0.0099405
ESE[Constant@Ya]    0.11988        0.016001
```

7.6 Example 5: cointegration analysis with dummies

The baseline DGP for this section is that used by Doornik, Hendry and Nielsen (1998), which is based on their model for the UK money demand:

$$
\Delta \mathbf{x}_t = \begin{pmatrix} -0.102 & 0 \\ 0 & -0.149 \\ 0 & 0.036 \\ 0 & -0.04 \end{pmatrix} \begin{pmatrix} 1 & -1 & 6.41 & 7.16 & 0 & -0.209 \\ 0 & 1 & -2.13 & 1.48 & -0.0063 & -11.186 \end{pmatrix}
$$

$$
\times \begin{pmatrix} \mathbf{x}_{t-1} \\ t \\ 1 \end{pmatrix} + \begin{pmatrix} 0.0063 \\ 0.0063 \\ 0 \\ 0 \end{pmatrix} + \begin{pmatrix} -0.3 & 0 & 0 & -0.06 \\ 0 & 0 & 0 & 0 \\ 0.068 & 0 & -0.26 & 0 \\ 0 & 0 & 0 & 0.17 \end{pmatrix} \Delta \mathbf{x}_{t-1} + \nu_t,
$$

when:

$$
\nu_t \sim \mathsf{IN}_4\left[0, \Sigma\right], \text{ where } \Sigma^* = \begin{pmatrix} 1.6\% & & & \\ -0.08 & 1\% & & \\ -0.51 & 0.03 & 0.69\% & \\ -0.49 & 0.09 & 0.31 & 1.3\% \end{pmatrix},
$$

using the lower triangle of Σ^* to show the cross correlations of the errors, and the diagonal for the standard errors (expressed as a percentage). The initial values are taken from the actual data:

$$
\begin{pmatrix} \mathbf{x}'_{-1} \\ \mathbf{x}'_0 \end{pmatrix} = \begin{pmatrix} 10.9445 & 11.1169 & 0.000779 & 0.048967 \\ 10.9369 & 11.1306 & 0.013567 & 0.050 \end{pmatrix}.
$$

Note that, despite the way the DGP is written, the constant is actually not restricted to the cointegration space. So the DGP has an unrestricted constant and a restricted trend, which precludes quadratic trend behaviour. The DGP thus satisfies $H_l(2)$ (see §2.3.4). A single replication of this DGP is analyzed in the tutorials of Doornik and Hendry (2001b). Here we consider the extension with dummies.

Implementing this DGP involves three features which have not been discussed yet. The first is using Y_2 in the General page to add a second lag to the DGP.

The next is the use of initial values, which are taken from the actual data:

General	YDGP	ZDGP	Errors	Model	Stats	Settings

Dy = A B' (y_1 : z) + A2 z + a3 + A5 Dy_1 + e

A		Ya	Yb	Yc	Yd
B	[-2]	10.9445	11.1169	0.000779	0.048967
A2	[-1]	10.9369	11.1306	0.013567	0.05
a3					
A5					
y_ini					

The specification of initial values can matter greatly in cointegrated systems. It is very easy to generate data, which, when plotted, look nowhere near actual economic data (for example, they are very close to straight lines). This is when the facility to plot the data can come in useful.

The third is the specification of the error variance matrix in the form of standard deviations and a correlation matrix:

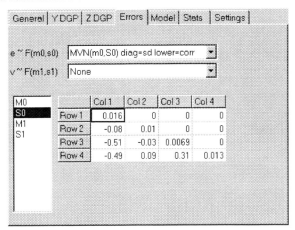

Running this experiment corresponds to a standard cointegration analysis, and the outcome is shown in Figure 7.7a.

For the next experiment, mark Customize Z in DGP on the General page. This will allow us generate the dummy variable, by writing Ox code to generate customized Z variables which enter the Y DGP. To add the code, click on the Customize button in the top-right corner of the Z DGP:

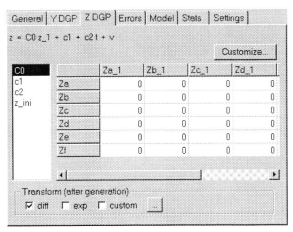

to activate the dialog in which the Ox code for the customization can be entered. The added code is:

```
decl mz = zeros(cT, m_cZ);   // same dimension as Z
if (cT > 48)
    mz[48][m_cZ-4] = 1;       // impulse dummy at T=49
if (cT > 54)
    mz[54][m_cZ-3] = 1;       // impulse dummy at T=55

if (cT > 48)
    mz[48:][m_cZ-2] = 1;      // step dummy at T=49
if (cT > 54)
    mz[54:][m_cZ-1] = 1;      // step dummy at T=55

return mz;
```

where cT is a function argument holding the sample size (including the number of discarded observations, which is zero here); m_cZ is the number of Z variables, which was set to six on the General page.

Note the distinction between customization and transformation:

- Customize requires activating the corresponding option on the General page. This allows changing the generated Z *before* they feed into the Y process.
- Other transformation applies the transformation *after* the data have been generated. Therefore, the generating processes are unaffected. However, the transformed variables can be used in the model.

The model adds two step dummies to the cointegrating space (the fifth and sixth: Ze and Zf, corresponding to mz[][m_cZ-2] and mz[][m_cZ-1] respectively, because Ox indexing starts at zero):

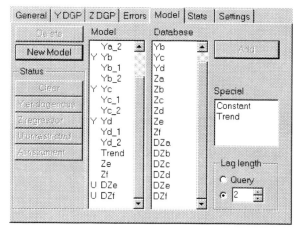

Figure 7.7 gives panels a and d of Figure 4 in Doornik, Hendry and Nielsen (1998), and show the impact of the dummy which is added to the model (despite being absent in the DGP). This is analogous to the effect of different treatments of the constant and trend.

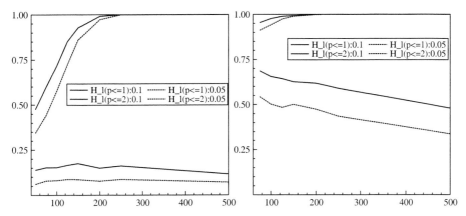

Figure 7.7 Doornik, Hendry and Nielsen (1998), part of Figure 4.

7.7 Example 6: structural breaks

To illustrate the implementation of structural breaks, we replicate one of the experiments of Hendry and Doornik (1997), also see Clements and Hendry (1999, §3.3.1).

The baseline DGP is the following I(0) VAR for a full-sample size of $T = 200$:

$$
\begin{aligned}
y_{1,t} &= \alpha_1 + 0.3y_{2,t} + \beta_1 y_{1,t-1} - 0.15y_{2,t-1} + \epsilon_{1,t}, \\
y_{2,t} &= \alpha_2 - 0.5y_{1,t-1} + 0.75y_{2,t-1} + \epsilon_{2,t}.
\end{aligned}
\tag{7.5}
$$

The $\{\epsilon_{i,t}\}$ are mutually and serially independent, normal, mean zero, with variances of 0.1, and 0.5 respectively. All breaks occurred at $T = 100$, followed by a return to the original parameter value at $T = 151$: the regime over $T = 100, \ldots, 150$ is denoted 2, the remaining regime is 1. The model is the first equation in (7.5), estimated consistently by OLS.[3] We used $M = 1000$ replications, with common random numbers across all experiments.

We only implement experiment C, which has a break in the dynamics of a non-zero mean I(0) process. The design parameter values for experiment C are:

	regime 1	regime 2
β_1	0.85	0.70
α_1	1.5	1.5
α_2	5.0	5.0

The key to implementing a DGP with breaks is to mark Break on the General page:

---

[3] Depending on the test statistic selected for analysis, non-centrality parameters could be calculated in this scalar I(0) process to reveal the factors determining test power.

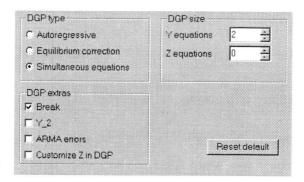

As a consequence, all coefficient matrices of the Y DGP have two versions, one for the period where the break is inactive, and one set for when it is in force. For those coefficients which are not affected, the corresponding matrices should be set to the same values. Here we show the values for the changed dynamics during the break period:

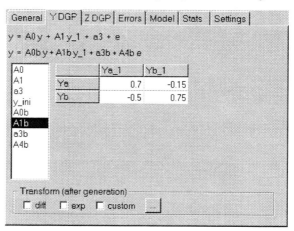

For the statistics select breakpoint and forecast Chow tests (see §2.3.4 for a description). Plot recursive rejection frequencies and the data. The latter is used as a visual check on the break.

We opted for recursive Monte Carlo in a step size of unity. This will take a while, but illustrate the fall in rejection frequency most clearly. The crucial aspect is to specify the period of the break: starting at $T = 100$ and finishing at $T = 150$ (so the break lasts for 51 observations).

We also set the number of forecasts is to 1. This way, the forecast Chow test will test against $T = 201$, thus ensuring that we get a meaningful value when estimating up to $T = 200$. The capture of the Settings page is shown below, with the final result in Figure 7.8.

Note that the 'jump' in the Yb process is *not* associated with any parameter non-constancy in the second equation, whereas the smaller change induces an easily detected break in the first equation. Also note how hard the second break is to detect once the first has happened and is not modelled.

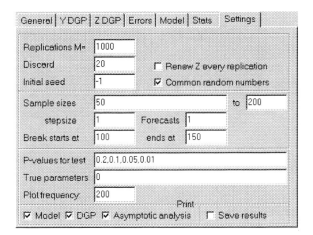

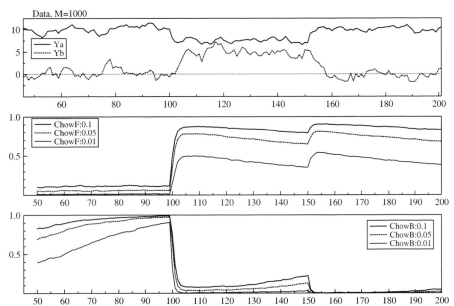

Figure 7.8 Hendry and Doornik (1997), experiment C: break in the dynamics.

Chapter 8

Tutorial on the General DGP

8.1 Introduction

The General DGP only differs from the PcNaive DGP, which was treated in the previous chapter, in the format which is used to specify the DGP. Model formulation, selection of statistics and setting the Monte Carlo parameters are all identical.

The DGP for this chapter is inspired by the DHSY model (Davidson, Hendry, Srba and Yeo, 1978), which is an equilibrium correction model for the logarithm of consumption, where the equilibrium correction is the gap between consumption and income, with an additional price term. What sets it aside from the previous DGP is that the DHSY model is seasonal: it uses fourth differences (the data are quarterly), and the equilibrium is towards the gap from a year ago. Implementing such a DGP requires more than two lags, which is not possible in the PcNaive DGP, but is in the General DGP.

Our stylized version of DHSY is:

$$
\begin{aligned}
\Delta_4 c_t &= -0.5\mu + 0.5\Delta_4 y_t - 0.1(c-y)_{t-4} + \tau\epsilon_{1t}, \\
\Delta_4 y_t &= \mu + \tau\epsilon_{2t},
\end{aligned}
\tag{8.1}
$$

using c_t for the logarithm of consumption, and y_t for log income. The parameters μ and τ will be specified shortly, and $\epsilon_{it} \sim N[0,1]$.

In levels, the DGP is:

$$
\begin{pmatrix} 1 & -0.5 \\ 0 & 1 \end{pmatrix} \begin{pmatrix} c_t \\ y_t \end{pmatrix} = \begin{pmatrix} 0.9 & -0.4 \\ 0 & 1 \end{pmatrix} \begin{pmatrix} c_{t-4} \\ y_{t-4} \end{pmatrix} + \begin{pmatrix} -0.5\mu \\ \mu \end{pmatrix} + \tau\epsilon_t,
$$

with corresponding reduced form:

$$
\begin{pmatrix} c_t \\ y_t \end{pmatrix} = \begin{pmatrix} 0.9 & 0.1 \\ 0 & 1 \end{pmatrix} \begin{pmatrix} c_{t-4} \\ y_{t-4} \end{pmatrix} + \begin{pmatrix} 0 \\ \mu \end{pmatrix} + \tau\nu_t, \quad \nu_t \sim N\left[0, \begin{pmatrix} 1.25 & 0.5 \\ 0.5 & 1 \end{pmatrix}\right]. \tag{8.2}
$$

This final expression is required because the DGP must be entered in reduced form. Figure 8.1 shows that the DGP is able to capture the changing seasonality well, although

76

other data features are not present (notably the lower seasonality of income). The data was generated using $\mu = 0.025$ and $\tau = 0.01$. An interesting class-room experiment is to change the values for μ and τ, and look at the effect on the generated data.

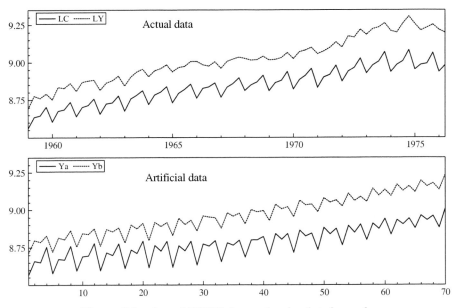

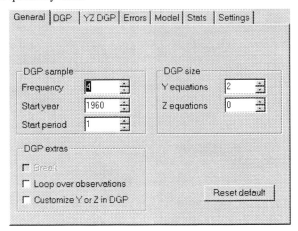

Figure 8.1   Actual DHSY data and a simulated sample.

8.2 Implementing the DGP

The General DGP allows for a sample start and frequency to be set. Here we start in 1960(1) and use quarterly data:

There are two equations, with *Ya* corresponding to the logarithm of consumption c_t, and *Yb* to the log of the income variable y_t.

The DGP is formulated in the same way as a model, which is for (8.2):

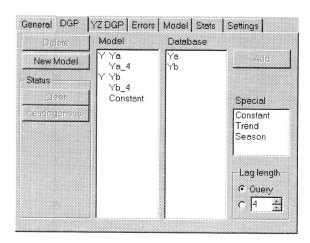

In the DGP all coefficients must be specified. For the general DGP without z variables:

$$\mathbf{y}_t = \mathbf{\Pi}\mathbf{w}_t + \mathbf{e}_t.$$

The coefficient matrix must be entered:

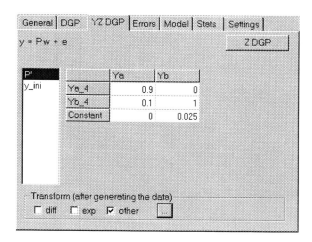

The button in the top right-hand corner switches between the Y DGP and the Z DGP.

To generate more realistic data, we condition on the actual data to start the data generation process. The DHSY database (which is supplied with PcGive) has:

	c_t	y_t
1959(1)	8.5610	8.6920
1959(2)	8.6355	8.7765
1959(3)	8.6465	8.7620
1959(4)	8.7043	8.7915

Without the different initial values for the seasonals, the seasonal pattern would look quite different. When we come to the Monte Carlo settings, we must remember to set the number of discarded observations to zero. Enter the initial values in the matrix editor:

P'		Ya	Yb
y_ini	[-4]	8.561	8.692
	[-3]	8.6355	8.7765
	[-2]	8.6465	8.762
	[-1]	8.7043	8.7915

Enter the error variance matrix for τ corresponding to 0.01:

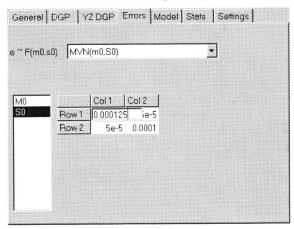

Initially, the model for estimation is specified in levels, corresponding to the DGP:

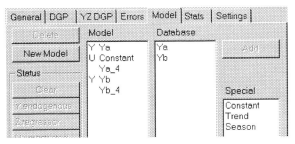

Select the coefficient from the statistics list, and the generated data from the available plots.

Finally, in the last page keep $M = 200$, set the starting and ending sample size to 66, and the number of discards to zero.

The resulting graph should match that in Figure 8.1b.

8.3 Specifying the equilibrium correction model

Estimating the equilibrium correction model requires the fourth differences $\Delta_4 c_t$, $\Delta_4 y_t$, as well as cointegrating vector $c_t - y_t$ in the database for modelling. So, check other in the Transform section, and click on the button with the ... to enter the code as follows:

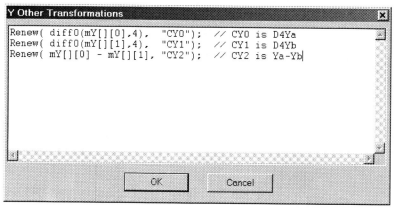

so that CY0,CY1,CY2, correspond to $\Delta_4 c_t$, $\Delta_4 y_t$, $c_t - y_t$ respectively. These variables are now available in the model (although we have to remember which variable is what: we are forced to use the names CY0, CY1 etc.):

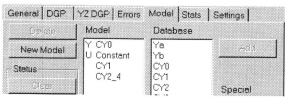

As always, there are many interesting experiments which can be considered. To conclude, we see what happens when the estimated model is mis-specified as:

$$\Delta c_t = \gamma_0 + \gamma_1 \Delta y_t + \gamma_2 (c_{t-1} - y_{t-1}) + \text{seasonals} + u_t.$$

The top two panels in Figure 8.2 show the distribution of the estimated coefficients when the model is correctly specified. Their horizontal scale is adjusted to the histogram of the mis-specified model in Figure 8.2c,d.

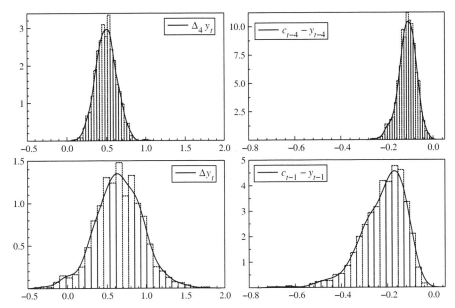

Figure 8.2 Comparison of correctly specified (a and b) and mis-specified model (c and d).

Chapter 9
Tutorial on the PcNaive Code

9.1 Introduction

This chapter gives a brief discussion on the structure of the programs generated by PcNaive. It will then show how you could add your own test statistics to the program. Added statistics become an integral part of the program, and will be listed on the Stats page. It is assumed that you already are a proficient Ox programmer, and understand the object-oriented features.

9.2 Program and class structure

At the base of each experiment are classes for simulation, data generation and estimation, which are all a standard part of the Ox system.

Figure 9.1   Program structure of a PcNaive program.

```
┌─────────────────────────────────────────────┐
│  ┌───────────────────────────────────────┐  │
│  │  simula.oxo[1], pcnaive.oxo[1], etc.  │  │
│  └───────────────────────────────────────┘  │
│                      ↓                        │
│  ┌───────────────────────────────────────┐  │
│  │         PcNaiveExe.ox[2]               │  │
│  └───────────────────────────────────────┘  │
│                      ↓                        │
│  ┌───────────────────────────────────────┐  │
│  │         PcNaiveExt.ox[2]               │  │
│  └───────────────────────────────────────┘  │
│                      ↓                        │
│  ┌───────────────────────────────────────┐  │
│  │       tutpcnaive04a.ox[3]              │  │
│  └───────────────────────────────────────┘  │
└─────────────────────────────────────────────┘
```

[1] Part of Ox, compiled code in ox/include.
[2] Part of PcNaive.
[3] The generated program.

Figure 9.1 shows the structure in terms of the required files. Figure 9.2 provides a schematic overview of the class structure.

Figure 9.2 Class structure of a PcNaive program.

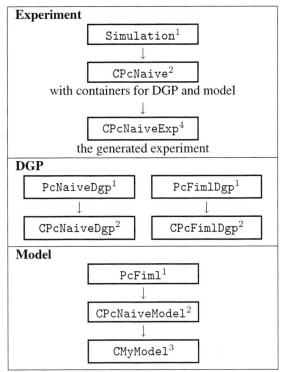

[1] Part of Ox, compiled code in ox/include, source in ox/src.
[2] Part of PcNaive, code in PcNaiveExe.ox.
[3] Part of PcNaive, code in PcNaiveExt.ox.
[4] In the generated program.

9.3 A generated program

This section lists the code for the tutpcnaive04a.ox tutorial example, and discusses some of the relevant features beneath each portion of code.

```
// File created by PcNaive on 20-02-2001 at 15:31:44
///////////////////////////////////////////////////////////
#include <packages/PcNaive/PcNaiveExt.ox>
```

The `PcNaiveExt.ox` file includes `PcNaiveExe.ox`, and the statement assumes that PcNaive is installed in `packages/PcNaive` (remember that you can use either \\ or / as a path separator in Ox).

```
class CPcNaiveExp : CPcNaive
{
    CPcNaiveExp();                        // constructor
    ~CPcNaiveExp();                       // destructor
    Generate(const iRep, const cT,  // generate replication
        const mxT);
    TransformY(const mY);
    TransformZ(const mZ);
};
```

This declares the class for the experiment. The `Generate` member function is called for each replication, see the Ox documentation of the `Simulation` class.

```
CPcNaiveExp::CPcNaiveExp()
{
    ranseed("LE");

    CPcNaive(<60:[20]120>+2, 20, 0, 1000, 1, -1, 1,
        <0.1,0.05>,
        <-0.1,0.3,0.5>);

    m_dgp = new CPcNaiveDgp(2, 1);  // create the DGP

    m_dgp.SetYParameter(
        <0,0.5;0,0>,
        <0.5,0;0,0.8>,
        <0;1>,
        <0;0>);
    m_dgp.SetUParameter(
        <-0.6,0;0,0>,
        <0,0;0,0>);
    m_dgp.SetZParameter(
        <0.75>,
        <0>,
        <0>);
    m_dgp.SetDistribution(U_DGP, MVNORMAL,
        <0;0>,
        <1,0.2;0.2,1>);
    m_dgp.SetDistribution(Z_DGP, MVNORMAL,
        <0>,
        <1>);

    SetRecursive(1);
```

```
    m_sys = new CMyModel();     // create the system/model
    CPcNaive::CreateData(2, 1);     // create the system database
                                // formulate the model
    m_sys.Select(Y_VAR, { "Ya", 0, 0} );
    m_sys.Select(Y_VAR, { "Ya", 1, 1} );
    m_sys.Select(Y_VAR, { "Ya", 2, 2} );
    m_sys.Select(X_VAR, { "Yb", 0, 0} );
    m_sys.Select(X_VAR, { "Yb", 1, 1} );
    m_sys.Select(U_VAR, { "Constant", 0, 0} );

    m_sys.SetEval(60, 120, 0);
    m_sys.AddEvalCoef(COEF_BETA, 0, 0);
    m_sys.AddEvalCoef(COEF_SERR, 0, 0);
    m_sys.AddEvalTest(TEST_AR, 0, 0);
    AddPlot(PLOT_RCOEF);
    AddPlot(PLOT_RPVAL);
    SetPlotStep(0);

    Update();
    println("PcNaive run: ", oxfilename(0));
    Report(1, 1, 1);
}
```

The constructor of the generated experiment sets all the parameters for the DGP and formulates the model. This example uses the CPcNaiveDgp, whereas an experiment based on the general DGP would use CPcFimlDgp.

```
CPcNaiveExp::~CPcNaiveExp()
{
    ~CPcNaive();                    // call base destructor
}
```

The destructor prints the final output, so must be called.

```
CPcNaiveExp::Generate(const iRep, const cT, const mxT)
{
    CPcNaive::Generate(iRep, cT, mxT);// update data

    m_sys.Estimate();               // estimate the model
                                    // get and store the statistics:
    m_mTest = m_sys.GetEvalTest();  // 2nd row: p-values
    m_mCoef = m_sys.GetEvalCoef();  // column vector
return TRUE;
}
```

The Generate function is called for each replication. The base class version, CPcNaive::Generate generates the data from the DGP, and stores it in the database of the model. Next, CPcNaiveExp::Generate estimates the model, and extracts the estimates and tests which were requested with calls to AddEvalCoef and AddEvalTest.

```
CPcNaiveExp::TransformY(const mY)
{
// mY is the T x n matrix with Y variables,
// There are 2n custom vars, "CY0" "CY1", ...;  e.g.:
// Renew( mY[][0] - mY[][1], "CY0"); // CY0 is Ya-Yb
}
CPcNaiveExp::TransformZ(const mZ)
{
// mZ is the T x q matrix with Z variables,
// There are 2q custom vars, "CZ0" "CZ1", ...;  e.g.:
// Renew( mZ[][0] - mZ[][1], "CZ0"); // CZ0 is Za-Zb
}
```

These functions are not used here, but implement custom transformations. They are called in `CPcNaive::Generate`, first for the ys, and then for the zs (but `TransformZ` is only called once if the z are not renewed at every replication).

```
main()
{
    decl exp = new CPcNaiveExp();
    exp.Simulate();
    delete exp;
}
```

Finally, `main` is where the program starts running, it creates an object of the class, calls `Simulate`, end then deletes the object. That's all.

9.4 Extending PcNaive

The structure of the code is such that it is relatively easy to add additional estimates or tests, in such a way that they appear to be an integrated part of PcNaive. The example used in this chapter will be to add a test for residual ARCH of first order.

```
#include <packages/PcNaive/PcNaiveExe.ox>

// NOTE: PcNaive reads this section, including comments !!
enum                 // COEF_{    indicates start
{
    coef_MY1 = coef_NEXT    // "my estimate"
};                   // COEF_}
enum                 // TEST_{    indicates start
{
    test_MY1 = test_NEXT    // "my test"
};                   // TEST_}
```

The `PcNaiveExt.ox` file in its default layout is just an empty shell. It starts with including the main PcNaive file, which is followed by the declaration of two enum fields, which just lists the constants representing the added estimates (COEF_...) and tests (TEST_...). This section is scanned by PcNaive, and any listed entries are added to the Stats page. Note that this process is case sensitive, and the example entries above are not seen by PcNaive because they are in lower case. In this case it just serves as a reminder to the programmer.

```
class CMyModel : CPcNaiveModel
{
    CMyModel();                              // constructor

    virtual GetCoefName(const eval);
    virtual GetTestName(const eval);
    virtual GetTestIsTwoSided(const eval);
    virtual GetCoef(const eval);
    virtual GetTest(const eval);
};
```

The file also defines the CMyModel class, which wraps around CPcNaiveModel. In its current format it does not do anything, but as soon as estimates or tests are added, it will define their behaviour.

In the function descriptions below, the eval argument is always one of the new constants which are defined in the enum statement (only the ones which are actually used in the experiment):

GetCoefName(const eval) Returns an array of strings with the names of the added COEF_...estimates. This is used in the final output and in labels of graphs.

GetTestName(const eval) Returns an array of strings with the names of the added TEST_ estimates. This is used in the final output and in labels of graphs.

GetTestIsTwoSided(const eval) Returns a row vector with a zero for each one-sided test, and one for two-sided tests.

GetCoef(const eval) Return a row vector with the actual COEF_ estimates. This is called for each replication.

GetTest(const eval) Returns a $2 \times c$ matrix with the TEST_ statistics in the first row, and p-values in the second row. This is called for each replication.

The objective here is to add the ARCH test, and the first step is to create the relevant constant. For this, only the section related to the tests is changed:

```
enum               // COEF_{    indicates start
{
    coef_MY1 = coef_NEXT   // "my estimate"
};                 // COEF_}
enum               // TEST_{    indicates start
{
    TEST_ARCH = test_NEXT  // "ARCH test"
};                 // TEST_}
```

TEST_ARCH is now the constant with which the ARCH test is identified (the user program would include an AddEvalTest(TEST_ARCH,0,0) statement). "ARCH test" is the entry which is added to the Stats page.

GetTestName and GetTestIsTwoSided are filled in:

```
CMyModel::GetTestName(const eval)
{
    // return an array of strings with the added TEST_ names
    if (eval == TEST_ARCH)
        return {"ARCH(1)"};
    else
        return {};
}
CMyModel::GetTestIsTwoSided(const eval)
{
    // return a row vector with a zero for each one-sided test,
    // and 1 for two-sided
    if (eval == TEST_ARCH)
        return <0>;
    else
        return <>;
}
```

Finally, the ARCH test must be computed. Here we use the function which is part of lib/testres, passing it the residuals of the estimated model, and as degrees of freedom adjustment $k - 1$.

```
CMyModel::GetTest(const eval)
{
    // return a 2 x c matrix with the TEST_ statistics in the
    // first row, and p-values in the second row
    if (eval == TEST_ARCH)
        return ArchTest(m_mResidual, 1, 1, m_cW - 1, FALSE);
    else
        return <>;
}
```

This requires that lib/testres is imported, and assumes the code is only used for single equation models. The resulting code is included as PcNaiveExt (example).ox. If you wish, you can try it by replacing PcNaiveExt.ox with this file (there is always PcNaiveExt (original).ox with the original version).

Part III

Learning Econometrics Using PcNaive

Chapter 10

Introduction

The objective of this part, based on Hendry (1990), is to suggest a number of themes in statistics and econometrics which can be explored easily in the classroom using PcNaive. The treatment is not intended to be comprehensive, either of the underlying subject-matter theory, or of the use of the program. Three levels of teaching are distinguished, from the elementary (Ch. 11), through intermediate (Ch. 12), to advanced (Ch. 13), corresponding loosely to the treatment of the subject in Hendry and Doornik (2001). Although this part is addressed to the teacher, it is equally valuable from the perspective of the student of Econometrics.

The topics covered under the first heading in §11.1–11.4 include the concept of variation, the shapes of statistical distributions, how sample size affects distributional shape (i.e., an introduction to convergence to normality from the uniform distribution), comparing t and normal distributions (two 'tight tailed' distributions), and a more serious example of a Central Limit theorem at work when observations are drawn from a skewed distribution. The examples become more like elementary econometrics in §11.6–11.11, beginning with a demonstration that bivariate regression theory really works, then evaluating the accuracy of estimated coefficient standard errors, moving on to fixed *versus* stochastic regressors, and applying that dichotomy to the issue of omitted variables where stochastic regressors compound bias and variance, discussing the effects of non-normal equation errors on regression, and concluding with an illustration of the effects of data measurement errors on regression biases and variances.

The intermediate level here is defined by the introduction of dynamics into econometrics, and the illustrations span §12.1–12.11. The first briefly considers the impact of time by noting the biases in estimated autoregressive coefficients, then moves on to the effects of autocorrelated errors in regression equations (static and dynamic). briefly noting inter-estimator comparisons between OLS and IV in a simultaneous system, the theory of Monte Carlo, and recursion in Monte Carlo applications, before turning to the impact of increasing sample size on test power. The level again rises in §12.8 with an analysis of 'nonsense regressions', showing the impact of evolution over time inducing misleading results, followed by Dickey–Fuller and Augmented Dickey–Fuller tests for unit roots, before the impact of dynamics on Chow test rejection frequencies is considered towards the end of the section, concluding with a look at invalid weak exogeneity in a cointegration equation.

Finally, the advanced ideas considered in §13.1–13.6.2 comprise a look at the role of asymptotic distribution theory in Monte Carlo, the distributions of inconsistent estimators, the impacts of structural breaks on econometric modelling, and testing the Lucas critique. The chapter ends by considering the problems that arise when there are no finite-sample moments of the entities being simulated: first when the error process has no moments, illustrated by the Cauchy distribution, concluding with an example where there are no moments in an instrumental variables estimator.

The PcNaive programs corresponding to the examples in this chapter are supplied with PcNaive:

teach01.ox	§11.7	teach06resar.ox	§12.2.1
teach02fix.ox	§11.8	teach06resar_dyn.ox	§12.2.2
teach02stoch.ox	§11.8	teach06resar_size.ox	§12.2.2
teach03fix.ox	§11.9	teach07power.ox	§12.6
teach03stoch.ox	§11.9	teach08chow.ox	§12.7
teach04exp.ox	§11.10	teach09nonsens*.ox	§12.8
teach04mis.ox	§11.10	teach09coint.ox	§12.11
teach04normal.ox	§11.10	teach10cauchy.ox	§13.6
teach05meas.ox	§11.11	teach10iv*.ox	§13.6.2
teach06ar1.ox	§12.1		

Chapter 11

Elementary Econometrics

11.1 The concept of variation

A non-negligible percentage of the students taught by the authors have experienced difficulties in understanding the basic concepts of variation and statistical distributions, despite their manifest appearance in everyday life by observable differences in heights, exam marks, incomes etc., across individuals. Since histograms tend to be included in school curricula, an additional help in illustrating variation is to show some histograms, and this can be done live in GiveWin very quickly for a wide range of distributions. An example would create a database in GiveWin with 1000 observations, and then create a normally distributed (using `rann()`) and uniformly distributed variable (using `ranu()`). The graphics facilities can then be used to draw the histogram. In the normal, very few instances are in the tails, whereas (of course) all values are equally likely for the uniform (so the presence of one small box reveals that the choice of intervals is not optimal here). These two distributions lead naturally to the next section, and point towards developing measures of dispersion and location.

11.2 Shapes of some statistical distributions

In addition to histograms, we can now draw the associated (non-parametrically estimated) density functions to highlight skewness, kurtosis etc. The illustration can e.g. be based on a $t(4)$ (created with `rant(4)` and the log-normal, which is easily created by exponentiating the standard normal variable. In the classroom, the density can be referred to as the 'population' with the histogram as the 'sample': obviously, this is incorrect, but at an elementary level, it would not help to introduce kernels! The GiveWin book has additional examples which can help to illustrate various distributions.

11.3 How sample size affects distributional shape

Once the course has reached the stage of considering sample means, the elementary effects of convergence to normality in well-behaved IID processes are easily illustrated (see Chapter 4). The example here is for the uniform variate in §11.1 above, beginning with the means of samples of size 1 in Fig. 11.1a, and 2 Fig. 11.1b (which estimates a triangular distribution). From then on the distributions 'looks' normal already, Fig. 11.1c and d have sample sizes 3 and 6 respectively. This is again easily graphed in GiveWin, using the following Algebra code:

```
mean1 = ranu();
mean2 = (mean1 + ranu()) / 2;
mean3 = (2 * mean2 + ranu()) / 3;
mean4 = (3 * mean3 + ranu()) / 4;
mean5 = (4 * mean4 + ranu()) / 5;
mean6 = (5 * mean5 + ranu()) / 6;
```

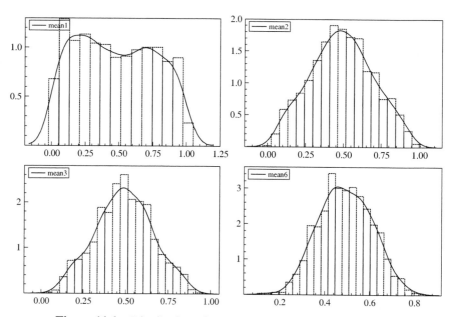

Figure 11.1 Distribution of sums of uniform random variables.

11.4 Comparing t and normal

Even elementary analyses of sampling behaviour need to explain how to estimate uncertainty in sample statistics, and in due course, how to test propositions about hypothesized population values of unknown parameters from sample evidence. There is obvious scope here for sampling experiments, illustrating rejection frequencies, measuring confidence intervals, and so on. A less stressed aspect conventionally is the importance of having 'tight tailed' distributions where genuine departures from the null are easy to distinguish. In 'fat tailed' distributions, such departures are hard to perceive since they must be distinguished in a welter of outliers. The normal, t and F (both for large degrees of freedom in the denominator) are all tight tailed (i.e., have few points beyond $\pm 3\sigma$); graphs can be used to illustrate the rapid convergence to zero in the tails. By way of contrast, show the $t(3)$ (for which only the first two moments exist): this distribution covers an enormous range. The choice of $t(3)$ also allows one to make a point about the hazards of inference in very small samples.

11.5 Convergence to normality: A Central Limit theorem at work

Since normality may seem (to students) to be a reasonable end point for symmetric distributions, but not when observations are drawn from a skewed distribution, this subsection extends §11.3 to highly-skewed distributions such as the exponential or log-normal. As for the uniform, GiveWin can be used to illustrate the disappearance of the skewness as more variables are averaged.

11.6 Bivariate regression theory really works

After explaining the theory for estimating the parameters of a bivariate regression from a hypothetical sample of data, students sometimes remain unable to link the theory formulae to real data and to the practical outcomes reported in journal articles.

Monte Carlo can be invaluable in bridging this gap. Consider the simplest single fixed regressor linear model without an intercept, generate data from it for a single realization and estimate the outcome. Since the population values of the coefficients are known to the students, they can see how close the outcome is to the anticipated result. Repeat this with a second data set drawn from the same process (i.e., with the same fixed regressor values, but new errors). Now extend to the Monte Carlo, drawing $M = 1000$ samples (replications) and consider the overall outcome. We applied PcNaive to this issue using the model:

$$y_t = \beta x_t + u_t \text{ where } u_t \sim \text{IN}\left[0, \sigma^2\right] \text{ over } t = 1, \ldots, T. \tag{11.1}$$

We set $\beta = 1$, $\sigma^2 = 1$ and $T = 60$, with $\{x_t\}$ generated as standard normal (independent from u_t, then held fixed across replications). The constant was omitted to simplify the algebra below, by not requiring deviations about the mean. The OLS estimator is given by:

$$\widehat{\beta} = \left(\sum_{t=1}^{T} x_t^2 \right)^{-1} \sum_{t=1}^{T} x_t y_t = \beta + \left(\sum_{t=1}^{T} x_t^2 \right)^{-1} \sum_{t=1}^{T} x_t u_t, \tag{11.2}$$

so that we have the theoretical result:

$$\mathsf{E}\left[\widehat{\beta}\right] = \beta + \mathsf{E}\left[\left(\sum_{t=1}^{T} x_t^2 \right)^{-1} \sum_{t=1}^{T} x_t u_t \right] = \beta + \left(\sum_{t=1}^{T} x_t^2 \right)^{-1} \sum_{t=1}^{T} x_t \mathsf{E}\left[u_t\right] = \beta. \tag{11.3}$$

Thus, on average, the OLS estimator should equal the true value, which is unity here.

The simulation results should convince even the most skeptical (the experiment is supplied as `teach01.ox`, also see Chapter 5):

$$\widehat{\mathsf{E}\left[\widehat{\beta}\right]} = 1.006 \ (0.004), \tag{11.4}$$

where the figure in parentheses is the Monte Carlo standard error (MCSE) which measures the uncertainty in the experiment, and tends to zero as $M \to \infty$. Regression estimation of a correctly specified model does indeed reproduce the population parameter value on average. The histogram (and perhaps interpolated density) of the empirical distribution can be used to highlight the variation about the population parameter. At a more advanced level, a similar approach can be applied to multiple regression, and is 'impressive' if the data generation process of the regressors is selected to ensure low simple correlations with the dependent variable (preferably 'wrong signed:' i.e. of the opposite sign to the regression coefficient), but high partial correlations. Moreover, it is easy to illustrate the invariance of the bias to the value of β by repeating the experiment for the same seed and $\{x_t\}$ but a different β.

11.7 The accuracy of estimated coefficient standard errors

The estimated coefficient variance in each replication (i.e. sample of data), based on the conventional theoretical formula (derived in (11.6) below), can be shown to be an extremely accurate estimator of the actual OLS sampling variance (across replications). Some Monte Carlo theory needs to be explained along the lines of Chapter 14 to enable this analysis to be comprehensible, but the outcome is worthwhile. Let:

$$\mathsf{V}\left[\widehat{\beta}\right] = \mathsf{E}\left[\left(\widehat{\beta} - \beta \right)^2 \right], \tag{11.5}$$

denote the correct sampling variance of $\widehat{\beta}$, then from the unbiasedness shown in (11.3):

$$
\begin{aligned}
\mathsf{V}\left[\widehat{\beta}\right] &= \mathsf{E}\left[\left\{\left(\textstyle\sum_{t=1}^{T} x_t^2\right)^{-1}\sum_{t=1}^{T} x_t u_t\right\}^2\right] \\
&= \left(\textstyle\sum_{t=1}^{T} x_t^2\right)^{-2}\mathsf{E}\left[\left(\textstyle\sum_{t=1}^{T} x_t u_t\right)^2\right] \\
&= \left(\textstyle\sum_{t=1}^{T} x_t^2\right)^{-2}\sum_{t=1}^{T}\sum_{s=1}^{T} x_t x_s \mathsf{E}\left[u_t u_s\right] \\
&= \sigma^2 \left(\textstyle\sum_{t=1}^{T} x_t^2\right)^{-2}\sum_{t=1}^{T} x_t^2 = \sigma^2 \left(\textstyle\sum_{t=1}^{T} x_t^2\right)^{-1},
\end{aligned}
\tag{11.6}
$$

since $\mathsf{E}[u_t u_s]$ is zero if $t \neq s$, and is σ^2 if $t = s$. Thus, as might have been anticipated from (11.2), since the regressor is fixed across samples, the variability of the error process (measured by σ^2) is directly communicated to that of the estimator, but mitigated by $\sum_{t=1}^{T} x_t^2$.

Next, we need an estimator of the coefficient variance in (11.6), which first requires an estimator of σ^2, given by:

$$
\widehat{\sigma}^2 = \sum_{t=1}^{T} \widehat{u}_t^2/(T-1) \text{ where } \widehat{u}_t = y_t - \widehat{\beta} x_t,
\tag{11.7}
$$

which can be shown to be unbiased for σ^2 (left as an exercise for students at this level). Then:

$$
\widehat{\mathsf{V}\left[\widehat{\beta}\right]} = \widehat{\sigma}^2 \left(\sum_{t=1}^{T} x_t^2\right)^{-1}
\tag{11.8}
$$

is also unbiased for $\mathsf{V}[\widehat{\beta}]$. The square root of (11.8) is the estimated standard error (ESE). Consequently, and more surprising, the variance of the estimator across samples can be estimated from a single sample using (11.7) and (11.8). However, both of (11.7) and (11.8) are statistics and hence have distributions themselves: our present interest is in finding how well regression theory works in practice. For example, how large is the variance of (11.8)? If it is very large relative to $\mathsf{V}[\widehat{\beta}]$, then inference will be unreliable in any given sample.

Simulating the model in §11.6 we have:

$$
\overline{\mathsf{ESE}} = 0.128\ (0.0004) \text{ whereas } \mathsf{MCSD} = 0.132.
\tag{11.9}
$$

The average of the square root of (11.8) is very close to the MCSD and to the asymptotic standard error (ASE) of $T^{-1/2} = 0.129$ with standard error $(TM)^{-1/2} = 0.0004$. The between-replications variability in the ESE is a small fraction (about 10%) of the mean value, so there is little need in practice to quote a standard error of a standard error. Indeed, this last point explains why the unbiasedness of the variance essentially holds for its square root. Finally, the mean value of $\widehat{\sigma}^2$ across replications is 0.995 (0.006), so it too is unbiased and well determined.

11.8 Fixed *versus* stochastic regressors

The next issue is extending these results to stochastic regressors, when the $\{x_t\}$ process is sampled independently in each replication. To also introduce the notion of a joint data density, and lead into §11.9, we allow for two regressors, denoted x_t and z_t respectively, so that the linear model of interest becomes:

$$y_t = \beta_1 x_t + \beta_2 z_t + u_t \text{ where } u_t \sim \text{IN} \left[0, \sigma^2\right]. \tag{11.10}$$

For fixed regressors, (11.10) is the DGP, but if the x_t, z_t are stochastic, we must consider the joint density of all the variables $\{y_t, x_t, z_t\}$, regarding (11.10) as determining the conditional density for $\{y_t | x_t, z_t\}$, and requiring a marginal process for $\{x_t, z_t\}$. Since the regressor variables must be generated in order to conduct the simulation study, Monte Carlo is a natural way to introduce the vital construct of a joint density and its factorization into conditional and marginal densities: an example is provided in (11.13) below. Here, we take the marginal density to be an independent normal with (vector) mean zero, variances of 1.0 and a correlation between x_t and z_t of 0.5.

The algebra of estimation for stochastic regressors is most easily explained in matrix form, or failing that, in scalar notation for a single regressor as follows. Equations (11.1) and (11.2) remain the same, but to establish unbiasedness, the idea of an overall expectation as the expectation (over a conditioning variable) of the conditional expectation is required, using the notation $|X$ to denote 'conditional on all observed values of x:

$$
\begin{aligned}
\mathsf{E}\left[\widehat{\beta}\right] &= \beta + \mathsf{E}\left[\left(\textstyle\sum_{t=1}^{T} x_t^2\right)^{-1} \sum_{t=1}^{T} x_t u_t\right] \\
&= \beta + \mathsf{E}_x\left[\mathsf{E}_u\left\{\left(\textstyle\sum_{t=1}^{T} x_t^2\right)^{-1} \sum_{t=1}^{T} x_t u_t\right\} \Big| X\right] \\
&= \beta + \mathsf{E}_x\left[0\right] = \beta,
\end{aligned}
\tag{11.11}
$$

since the term in braces $\{\cdot\}$ vanishes as in (11.2).

The corresponding analysis applied to $\mathsf{E}[(\widehat{\beta} - \beta)^2]$ leads to:

$$\mathsf{V}\left[\widehat{\beta}\right] = \sigma^2 \mathsf{E}\left[\left(\sum_{t=1}^{T} x_t^2\right)^{-1}\right] \neq \sigma^2 \left(\mathsf{E}\left[\sum_{t=1}^{T} x_t^2\right]\right)^{-1} \tag{11.12}$$

The precise outcome in (11.12) is less easy to explain in an elementary course, but it is worth noting the last inequality, and commenting that nevertheless the two expressions will be equal for fixed Xs, and approximately equal when the variance of $\sum_{t=1}^{T} x_t^2$ is small. The Monte Carlo simulation produced:

	Fixed				Stochastic			
	Bias	MCSE	MCSD	ESE	Bias	MCSE	MCSD	ESE
β_1	−0.003	0.005	0.145	0.143	−0.0004	0.005	0.153	0.151
β_2	−0.004	0.005	0.152	0.147	−0.006	0.005	0.156	0.152

Thus, the bias is indeed small and insignificant in both cases, the Monte Carlo results are precise (small MCSEs), the MCSD and ESE remain very close and the mean $\hat{\sigma}^2$ is extremely close to the true value (mean $0.993, 0.996$ for fixed and stochastic respectively, its MCSE was only 0.006). The instructor might note that for the DGP parameter values selected above, the ESEs of the estimators are close to the theoretical value of 0.149 (since $|E[\mathbf{X}'\mathbf{X}]|$ is $3/4$).

11.9 Omitted variables: compounding bias and variance

An important motivation behind suggesting using two regressors in §11.8 is to move on to consider the consequences of incorrectly omitting one of them. It is at this stage that fixed and stochastic regressor assumptions begin to entail very different implications. To progress, we first factorize the marginal density of the two regressors into the conditional density of the omitted one (here z_t) given the included regressor, times the marginal of the included variable x_t:

$$D_{x,z}(x_t, z_t) = D_{z|x}(z_t \mid x_t) \cdot D_x(x_t). \tag{11.13}$$

Since the joint density is normal, the first factor yields a linear model, which we denote by:

$$z_t = Bx_t + v_t \quad \text{where} \quad v_t \sim \text{IN}\left[0, \sigma_v^2\right]. \tag{11.14}$$

The unknown coefficient B can be estimated by:

$$\widehat{B} = \left(\sum_{t=1}^{T} x_t^2\right)^{-1} \sum_{t=1}^{T} x_t z_t, \tag{11.15}$$

which the earlier analysis shows is unbiased for B. In the present Monte Carlo, $B = 0.5$ (the same as the correlation) and v_t has a variance of 0.75. Consider estimating over $t = 1, \ldots, T$:

$$y_t = \gamma_1 x_t + w_t \quad \text{where it is claimed that} \quad w_t \sim \text{IN}\left[0, \sigma_w^2\right]. \tag{11.16}$$

We use $\tilde{\ }$ to denote estimators relative to (11.16). Since:

$$
\begin{aligned}
\tilde{\gamma}_1 &= \left(\sum_{t=1}^{T} x_t^2\right)^{-1} \sum_{t=1}^{T} x_t y_t \\
&= \beta_1 + \left(\sum_{t=1}^{T} x_t^2\right)^{-1} \sum_{t=1}^{T} x_t z_t \beta_2 + \left(\sum_{t=1}^{T} x_t^2\right)^{-1} \sum_{t=1}^{T} x_t u_t,
\end{aligned} \tag{11.17}
$$

where we have used (11.10), it is easy to show that:

$$E\left[\tilde{\gamma}_1\right] = \beta_1 + B\beta_2 = \gamma_1. \tag{11.18}$$

Equation (11.18) holds for both fixed and stochastic regressors, where $B \equiv \widehat{B}$ in the former. We view $\widetilde{\gamma}_1$ as an unbiased estimator of γ_1 in the reparametrized model (11.16), but it is also a biased estimator of β_1 in (11.10) with bias given by $B\beta_2$.

The important difference between fixed and stochastic regressors arises in their theoretically anticipated variances:

$$E\left[(\widetilde{\gamma}_1 - \gamma_1)^2\right] = E\left[\left\{\left(\widehat{B} - B\right)\beta_2 + \left(\sum_{t=1}^{T} x_t^2\right)^{-1}\sum_{t=1}^{T} x_t u_t\right\}^2\right]. \tag{11.19}$$

The first term in braces vanishes for fixed regressors, but contributes to the regression-coefficient variance for stochastic regressors, yielding the general result:

$$V[\widetilde{\gamma}_1] = \beta_2^2 V\left[\widehat{B}\right] + \sigma^2 E\left[\left(\sum_{t=1}^{T} x_t^2\right)^{-1}\right] = (\sigma^2 + \beta_2^2 \sigma_v^2)E\left[\left(\sum_{t=1}^{T} x_t^2\right)^{-1}\right], \tag{11.20}$$

using (11.12) for both the second term and $V[\widehat{B}]$.

Moreover, the estimator of σ^2 from (11.16) is biased, although this is tedious to show without using matrix algebra. Let $\mathbf{z} = (z_1 \ldots z_T)'$ and let $\mathbf{Q}_x = \mathbf{I}_T - \mathbf{x}(\mathbf{x}'\mathbf{x})^{-1}\mathbf{x}'$, then:

$$E\left[\widetilde{\sigma}^2\right] = \sigma^2 + \beta_2^2 E\left[\mathbf{z}'\mathbf{Q}_x\mathbf{z}\right]/(T-1) = \sigma^2 + \beta_2^2 \sigma_v^2. \tag{11.21}$$

Note that $\mathbf{Q}_x$ is the idempotent matrix which annihilates $\mathbf{x}$: $\mathbf{Q}_x\mathbf{x} = \mathbf{0}$.

The estimation formula for the coefficient variance calculated by any computer program for OLS is:

$$\widetilde{V[\widetilde{\gamma}_1]} = \widetilde{\sigma}^2 \left(\sum_{t=1}^{T} x_t^2\right)^{-1}, \tag{11.22}$$

and this will have the expected value:

$$E\left[\widetilde{V[\widetilde{\gamma}_1]}\right] = (\sigma^2 + \beta_2^2 \sigma_v^2)E\left[\left(\sum_{t=1}^{T} x_t^2\right)^{-1}\right]. \tag{11.23}$$

For fixed regressors, $V[\widehat{B}]$ is zero and so (11.20) coincides with the formula obtained under the assumption of correct specification. However, σ_v^2 is non-zero in both cases, so the estimator of (11.20) based on (11.23) is biased for fixed regressors (as is $\widetilde{\sigma}^2$ for σ^2 in both cases).

It is important that students fully understand this result: under mis-specification, the population parameters (β, σ^2 etc) are different from the expected values of the corresponding statistics (as in (11.20) and (11.21)); and the expected values of the estimation formulae, which are the entities calculated in practice, may differ from those derived under the assumption of correct specification (as in (11.23)). The great advantage of a Monte Carlo is that all the relevant values are either known or can be obtained by simulation to clarify their differences, and their empirical counterparts.

The present Monte Carlo yielded the following outcomes:

	Fixed				Stochastic			
	Bias	MCSE	MCSD	ESE	Bias	MCSE	MCSD	ESE
γ_1	0.419	0.004	0.132	0.171	0.492	0.005	0.172	0.171

All of the predicted consequences emerge: the bias in $\widetilde{\gamma}_1$ is not significantly different from the value given by (11.18) (i.e., 0.5);[1] ESE is biased for MCSD under fixed regressors, but not under stochastic — hence, the MCSD is smaller for fixed regressors; and the mean value of $\widetilde{\sigma}^2$ is almost exactly that entailed by (11.21) (i.e., 1.75). It should be clear to the students what happens when the correlation is set to zero — and a Monte Carlo experiment will confirm that.

11.10 The effects of non-normal equation errors

The above results on bias, or its absence, did not depend directly on normality (except for the derivation of the conditional model as linear, so a linear process must be substituted for that step). However, small-sample inference can be substantially affected by non-normal errors. In this section, we compute the confidence intervals for $\widehat{\beta}$ from (11.1) but with an intercept, first for normal errors, and then for exponentially distributed errors. An alternative interesting simulation is the comparison of log and linear approximations: run the first experiment twice, where in the second run, the exponentials of the data variables are used (i.e., the functional form is mis-specified).

Thus, add an intercept to (11.1), denoted κ, generate the data as before with $u_t \sim N[0,1]$ and repeat the experiment with $u_t \sim \exp(1)$. The intercept will correct for the fact that in the second experiment, $E[u_t] = 1$, whereas in both experiments, $V[u_t] = 1$. Figure 11.2a and b respectively show the histograms (with estimated density functions) for the two experiments, from which it is visually apparent that both are close to normality. Further, the rejection frequencies of the t-tests of $H_0: \beta = \beta_0$ (the population value) were insignificantly different from 5% in both cases. This finding contrasts with the properties of the distributions for the error processes, where the latter is highly skewed, whereas we know the former is symmetric. Figure 11.2c shows the histogram of the t-tests with normal errors, but functional form mis-specification.

---

[1]There is a slight problem for the instructor to explain here. Under fixed regressors, the precise correlation between x and z will differ from 0.5 due to the vagaries of sampling in the one replication generating the data. Thus, one could save the data set from the Monte Carlo, compute the empirical correlation/regression of z_t on x_t, and calculate the bias using that value for B.

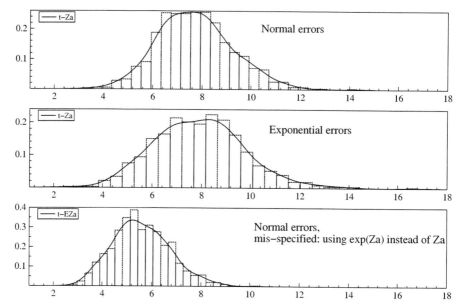

Figure 11.2   Distribution of t-tests for normal errors, exponential errors, and mis-specified functional form.

Such an outcome was predictable from the results of §11.5, since the present regression example is only a minor extension thereof, and is subject to the same underlying central limit forces.

11.11 The effects of data measurement errors

The final example, from the many that could have been studied, is the impact of measurement errors superimposed between the generated and the observed values of the random variables in regression models. We retain (11.1) for simplicity, but with a stochastic regressor:[2]

$$x_t = z_t + e_t \text{ where } z_t \sim \text{IN}\left[0, \sigma_z^2\right], \quad e_t \sim \text{IU}\left[-h, h\right], \quad \text{E}[z_t e_t] = 0, \qquad (11.24)$$

and z_t is the systematic component which actually generated y_t, whereas e_t is a pure error of measurement relative to the determination of y_t in the DGP:

$$y_t = \beta z_t + u_t \text{ where } u_t \sim \text{IN}\left[0, \sigma_u^2\right]. \qquad (11.25)$$

The fitted regression is:

$$y_t = \delta x_t + \epsilon_t \text{ where it is claimed that } \epsilon_t \sim \text{IN}\left[0, \sigma^2\right]. \qquad (11.26)$$

---

[2]In the PcNaive DGP select three ys: explain Ya by Yb in the DGP and relate Yc to Yb. Regress Ya on Yc in the model.

The first important point is that if (11.26) is a regression, then it is defined by:

$$E\left[y_t \mid x_t\right] = \delta x_t \text{ where } E\left[x_t \epsilon_t\right] = 0. \tag{11.27}$$

This equation determines the value of δ, since from (11.27), for a normal process:

$$\begin{aligned}
\delta &= E\left[y_t x_t\right]/E\left[x_t^2\right] \\
&= E\left[(\beta z_t + u_t)(z_t + e_t)\right]/E\left[(z_t + e_t)^2\right] \\
&= \beta E\left[z_t^2\right]/\left(E\left[z_t^2\right] + E\left[e_t^2\right]\right) \tag{11.28}
\end{aligned}$$

We chose $\beta = 1$, $\sigma_z^2 = 2$ and $h = 2$, so that $E[e_t^2] = 4/3$, which entails that $\delta = 0.6$. Such a large bias for β is unsurprising when it is noted that the measurement error variance is 66% of the systematic variance so that 40% of the observed data variance is due to measurement error. The Monte Carlo findings for $T = 60$ are:

	Mean	Bias	MCSE	MCSD	ESE
δ	0.602	−0.398	0.003	0.090	0.096
$\widetilde{\sigma}^2$	1.807			0.326	

Again there is a close match between simulation and theory. The biases are much smaller for more reasonable sizes of white-noise errors of measurement (e.g., 5% to 10% of the observed variance). The irrelevance of white-noise measurement errors on y_t in static regressions is also easily shown.

If the above statistical theory is deemed too demanding for the relevant group of students, the consequences of all of the specification errors can still be demonstrated numerically. Conversely, for mathematically better-qualified groups, the examples can be extended (e.g. using instrumental variables in (11.26) etc.).

Chapter 12

Intermediate econometrics

The examples in the two preceding sections were for static DGPs, and the defining characteristic of this section is the generalization to time dependent (dynamic) processes. The first example is very well known.

12.1 The impact of time: bias in autoregressive model estimation

The analysis of the first-order autoregressive model was presented in §§14.3.1,14.3.2: here, we merely record our view that it is an excellent teaching example both for illustrating asymptotic distribution theory in action (the bias and skewness of the distribution vanish as the sample size increases), and for introducing dynamics. Since a working knowledge of the first-order autoregressive model is a necessary prerequisite for the next subsection, we summarize the asymptotic theory and the outcome for a sample size of $T = 1000$, deliberately picked so large that the limiting distribution is attained. The DGP is:

$$y_t = \alpha y_{t-1} + \epsilon_t \text{ with } \epsilon_t \sim \text{IN}\left[0, \sigma^2\right], \quad (12.1)$$

where $|\alpha| < 1$ and $y_0 = 0$. The OLS estimator of α is:

$$\widehat{\alpha} = \sum_{t=1}^{T} y_t y_{t-1} / \sum_{t=1}^{T} y_{t-1}^2, \quad (12.2)$$

which has the large sample distribution:

$$\sqrt{T}\left(\widehat{\alpha} - \alpha\right) \xrightarrow{D} \text{N}\left[0, \left(1 - \alpha^2\right)\right]. \quad (12.3)$$

Thus, approximately, for large T:

$$\widehat{\alpha} \underset{app}{\sim} \text{N}\left[\alpha, \frac{\left(1 - \alpha^2\right)}{T}\right]. \quad (12.4)$$

The Monte Carlo matches well, for $\alpha = 0.5$ and $M = 200$, we have:

	Mean	Bias	MCSE	MCSD	ESE
α	0.497	−0.003	0.002	0.026	0.027
$\widetilde{\sigma}^2$	0.996			0.048	

when the theoretical coefficient standard error is 0.0274.

12.2 Autocorrelated errors in regression equations

The focus in this section is on the consequences of untreated residual autocorrelation which is generated by a valid common factor equation (called COMFAC: see Sargan, 1980b, Hendry and Mizon, 1978, and Hendry, 1995b for COMFAC theory and modelling procedures). The main justification for studying the consequences of untreated residual autocorrelation is to motivate students not to let it happen. As earlier, the consequences depend on whether the model is static or includes lagged endogenous variables (or any variables that are Granger-caused by the dependent variable: see Granger, 1969).

12.2.1 Biased variance in a static model

The algebra of this case is presented in most standard textbooks (see e.g., Maddala, 1977). We retain equation (11.1) but replace the assumptions about the $\{u_t\}$ by:

$$u_t = \rho u_{t-1} + v_t \quad \text{where } v_t \sim \text{IN} \left[0, \sigma_v^2\right] \text{ and } |\rho| < 1. \tag{12.5}$$

It is easy to show that the OLS estimator remains unbiased (a useful student exercise) but that the variance is given by:

$$
\begin{aligned}
\mathsf{V}\left[\widehat{\beta}\right] &= \mathsf{E}\left[\left\{\left(\sum_{t=1}^{T} x_t^2\right)^{-1}\left(\sum_{t=1}^{T} x_t u_t\right)\right\}^2\right] \\
&= \left(\sum_{t=1}^{T} x_t^2\right)^{-2} \mathsf{E}\left[\left(\sum_{t=1}^{T} x_t u_t\right)^2\right] \\
&= \left(\sum_{t=1}^{T} x_t^2\right)^{-2}\left(\sum_{t=1}^{T}\sum_{s=1}^{T} x_t x_s \mathsf{E}\left[u_t u_s\right]\right) \\
&= \sigma_u^2 \left(\sum_{t=1}^{T} x_t^2\right)^{-2} \sum_{t=1}^{T}\sum_{s=1}^{T} \rho^{|t-s|} x_t x_s,
\end{aligned}
\tag{12.6}
$$

since $\mathsf{E}\left[u_t u_s\right] = \sigma_u^2 \rho^{|t-s|}$ where $\sigma_u^2 = \sigma_v^2/(1-\rho^2)$.

A more explicit formula can be derived by taking the $\{x_t\}$ to be a first-order autoregression also:

$$x_t = \lambda x_{t-1} + w_t \quad \text{where } w_t \sim \text{IN} \left[0, \sigma_w^2\right] \text{ and } |\lambda| < 1, \tag{12.7}$$

so that:

$$\mathsf{E}\left[x_t x_s\right] = \sigma_x^2 \lambda^{|t-s|} \quad \text{where} \quad \sigma_x^2 = \frac{\sigma_w^2}{1 - \lambda^2}. \tag{12.8}$$

Then, to a first approximation:

$$\mathsf{V}\left[\widehat{\beta}\right] = T^{-1} \frac{\sigma_u^2 (1 + \rho\lambda)}{\sigma_x^2 (1 - \rho\lambda)}. \tag{12.9}$$

If $\rho = 0.8$, $\lambda = 0.9$, $\sigma_\nu^2 = 1$ and $\sigma_w^2 = 2$, then:

$$\mathsf{V}\left[\widehat{\beta}\right] = 1.62/T. \tag{12.10}$$

This contrasts with the value of the conventionally-calculated formula, allowing only for the bias in the estimator of the equation error variance, given by:

$$\mathsf{E}\left[\widehat{\sigma}^2\right] = \frac{\sigma_\nu^2}{1 - \rho^2} \left[1 - T^{-1} \frac{(1 + \rho\lambda)}{(1 - \rho\lambda)}\right] \approx \frac{\sigma_\nu^2}{1 - \rho^2} = \sigma_u^2, \tag{12.11}$$

so that:

$$\mathsf{E}\left[\widehat{\mathsf{V}\left[\widehat{\beta}\right]}\right] = \mathsf{E}\left[\widehat{\sigma}^2 \left(\sum_{t=1}^{T} x_{1,t}^2\right)^{-1}\right] = \frac{1}{T} \frac{\sigma_\nu^2 (1 - \lambda^2)}{\sigma_w^2 (1 - \rho^2)} \left[1 - \frac{1}{T} \frac{(1 + \rho\lambda)}{(1 - \rho\lambda)}\right] \approx \frac{\sigma_u^2}{\sigma_x^2}. \tag{12.12}$$

For the parameter values used in evaluating (12.9), (12.12) yields (keeping the term of T^{-2}):

$$\mathsf{E}\left[\widehat{\mathsf{V}\left[\widehat{\beta}\right]}\right] = 0.53 T^{-1} \left(1 - 6.14 T^{-1}\right). \tag{12.13}$$

At $T = 40$, (12.10) yields 0.041 for the correct sampling variance (and so 0.202 for the standard deviation), whereas (12.13) yields 0.011 (i.e., 0.104 for the ESE), which is smaller by a factor of almost four. The Monte Carlo confirms these approximations: the MCSD is 0.200 and the Monte Carlo ESE is 0.086 (0.001), using 1000 replications. Also of note, the estimator of β is not significantly biased, but the t-test of H_0: $\beta = \beta_0$ rejects 39% of the time when the nominal size is 5%, so inference is completely unreliable.

12.2.2 Biased coefficients in dynamic models

The econometric algebra, and the implications, become even more unpleasant if the basic equation is dynamic, with at least one additional regressor to ensure unique identification of the parameters. We maintain (12.5), but extend the linear equation of interest to:

$$y_t = \beta_1 y_{t-1} + \beta_2 x_t + u_t \quad \text{where} \quad |\beta_1| < 1. \tag{12.14}$$

It is easy to show that:

$$E\left[y_{t-1}u_t\right] = \rho E\left[y_t u_t\right] = \rho E\left[\beta_1 y_{t-1}u_t + u_t^2\right] = \rho \frac{\sigma_u^2}{1 - \rho \beta_1}, \tag{12.15}$$

which must be non-zero when $\rho \neq 0$, inducing an inconsistency (and associated finite-sample bias) in the OLS estimator applied to (12.14). However, deriving the bias is beyond most courses at this level, and even the inconsistency is a little tedious. We have now reached situations where Monte Carlo is beginning to have a comparative advantage in teaching economics students who do not wish to specialize in econometrics, although the formulae are, of course, well known for most of the problems we consider in this chapter. PcNaive can calculate the numerical values of the plims as shown in the following table.

In the Monte Carlo simulation, we set $\beta_1 = 0.6$, $\beta_2 = 1$ and $\rho = 0.8$, using:

$$x_t = 0.8x_{t-1} + w_t \text{ where } w_t \sim \text{IN}\left[0, 1\right].$$

keeping (12.5) with $\sigma_\nu^2 = 1$ as before. The results for $M = 1000$, $T = 1000$ were:

	plim	Mean	Bias	MCSE	MCSD	ESE	ASE
β_1	0.817	0.815	0.216	0.0005	0.016	0.0098	0.0097
β_2	0.576	0.580	−0.420	0.0015	0.048	0.0268	0.0267
$\tilde{\sigma}^2$	1.852	1.847			0.120		

The biases in the coefficients are almost 20% and are close to the plims. Also, the ESEs are close to the ASEs but far from the MCSDs.

This example has many extensions concerning the powers of residual autocorrelation tests, invalid inference with autocorrelated errors, contrasts and similarities between autoregressive and moving-average errors, and so on. For example, if recursive procedures have been introduced, the changing finite-sample biases deserve note, as do the horrific Chow test rejection frequencies.

12.3 Inter-estimator comparisons: OLS and IV in a simultaneous system

This is noted for completeness: illustrations are in §7.5 and the next chapter.

12.4 The theory of Monte Carlo

Chapter 14 provides the relevant background. The main concepts are worth establishing for their value in econometric thinking in general. Our experience is that although the basic theorem of Chapter 14 is easily understood, its application to all sorts of functions of econometric statistics being made into the $\{x_i\}$ of the Monte Carlo is not easily grasped. For example, it can take students some time to understand the difference between the MCSD and the ESE, and especially the standard error of the ESE, owing to the latter being computed in each replication of the simulation, and so having a distribution across replications.

12.5 Recursion in Monte Carlo applications

Once more, this subsection merely points in a possible direction, which Chapter 14 discusses in detail and Chapter 6 illustrates.

12.6 Test power: the impact of increasing sample size

Power functions are rarely calculated in econometric texts, yet are easy to obtain either numerically, using the type of asymptotic local approximation discussed in Chapter 16 (see the figures therein), or can be simulated (see e.g., Mizon and Hendry, 1980). The example in Chapter 6 is for a first-order autoregression, such as (12.7) above, where interest centers on the power of the t-test to reject the null hypothesis that $\lambda = 0$, when the true value of λ is 0.5 (σ_w^2 can be set to unity without loss of generality). Many other examples are possible, either using recursive procedures to illustrate the impact of increasing sample size with a fixed test significance level and a false null (i.e., showing test consistency), or conducting a batch study at different parameter values and/or significance levels.

Figure 12.1 presents graphs for $T = 10, \ldots, 60$ of the rejection frequency of H_0: $\beta = 0$ in (11.1) when $\beta = 0.3$ and $\{x_t\}$ is stochastic using a test size of $\alpha = 0.05$. The smaller β value than §10 was selected to let the power function span a greater range, but otherwise the experiment is the same as in (11.1). The simulation was based on a Monte Carlo sample of 1000 replications, whereas the local approximation used:[1]

$$T\widehat{\beta}^2 / \widehat{\mathsf{V}\left[\widehat{\beta}\right]} \sim \chi^2(1, \varphi) \quad \text{where} \quad \varphi = T\beta^2 \mathsf{m}/\sigma^2 \quad \text{and} \quad \mathsf{m} = T^{-1}\mathsf{E}\left[\sum_{t=1}^{T} x_t^2\right],$$

where φ is the non-centrality parameter. Note that $\varphi = 0.09T$ and $\mathsf{m} = 1$. As can be seen, both lines illustrate the increasing power to reject the false null at a fixed significance level as the sample size increases. While they increase at the same rate, which here is the best measure of the accuracy of the approximation, the simulation outcome is always smaller due to using the correct critical value at each sample size, whereas the approximation uses the fixed asymptotic (or nominal) value of 3.84.

---

[1] The Ox pseudo-expression `1 - probchi(3.8415, 1, `φ`)` can be used to evaluate the power function.

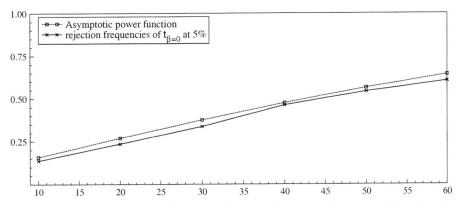

Figure 12.1 Monte Carlo and asymptotic power functions for t-test of $H_0 : \beta = 0$.

12.7 The impact of dynamics on Chow test rejection frequencies

The Chow (1960) test for predictive failure is an example of a large class of widely-used tests whose justification is either based on fixed regressor model analysis, or relies on asymptotic approximations. For practical work, it is important to know how good such approximations are in general, and Monte Carlo study of DGPs analogous to the models used in applied research can shed useful light on such issues. Here, we merely illustrate the approach for the break-point test ($N\downarrow$ in PcGive) at one point in the parameter space of a first-order autoregression with coefficient 0.5 and an econometric sample size of $10, 11, \ldots, 60$, using 1000 replications. Since the null of no break is true and the critical values used correspond to a nominal size of 5%, the standard error of an independent probability estimate (from the binomial) is $\sqrt{[p(1 - p)/M]} = 0.007$, the anticipated spread around 0.05 is $[0.036, 0.064]$; all the observed rejection frequencies lie inside that interval. Figure 12.2 illustrates: it shows the 5% and 10% rejection frequencies, with more detail in the inset. Note that the zero outcome for $T = 60$ is an artefact of the test: there is no post break-point data.

12.8 Nonsense regressions: the impact of evolution over time

When $\alpha = 1$ in the autoregressive process (12.1), the process is said to have a *unit root*. The presence of unit roots affects the statistical distributions of many tests, and failure to take this into account can therefore seriously distort statistical inference. Because many economic time-series appear to have a unit root (and some even appear to have two), this has become an important area of research, with many results now part of the

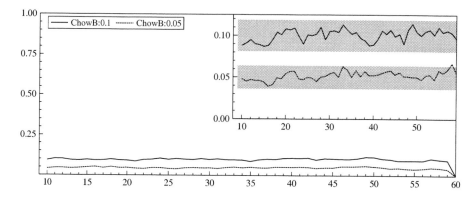

Figure 12.2   Break-point Chow test rejection frequencies.

standard econometric curriculum.

When $\alpha = 1$ in (12.1), we can write:

$$\Delta y_t \equiv y_t - y_{t-1} = \epsilon_t \ \text{ with } \ \epsilon_t \sim \text{IN} \left[0, \sigma^2 \right], \tag{12.16}$$

assuming $y_0 = 0$. The time-series for y_t looks quite different from a stationary process (which has $|\alpha| < 1$), and PcNaive can be used to show graphs of the data for various α.

To illustrate the consequences of unit roots, we use the following setup:

$y_t = \alpha y_{t-1} + \epsilon_t,$	$\epsilon_t \sim \text{N}[0, 1]$	
$x_t = \gamma x_{t-1} + v_t,$	$v_t \sim \text{N}[0, 1], \ \text{E}[\epsilon_t v_t] = 0$	
Case	DGP	econometric model
a	$\alpha = \gamma = 0$	$y_t = \beta_1 x_t + u_t$
b	$\alpha = \gamma = 1$	$y_t = \beta_1 x_t + u_t$
c	$\alpha = \gamma = 0.2$	$y_t = \delta_1 y_{t-1} + \beta_1 x_t + \delta_2 x_{t-1} + u_t$

In addition, the cointegrated case is considered, but explained later.

Figure 12.3 reports the frequency distributions of the t-tests from a simulation study using $M = 10\,000$ drawings for $T = 50$. The shaded boxes are for ± 2, which is the approximate conventional 95% confidence interval. The first panel (a) shows the distribution of the t-test on the coefficient of x_t in a regression of y_t on x_t when both variables are white noise and unrelated (case a in the table). This is numerically very close to the correct distribution of a t-variable. The second panel (denoted b, in the top row) shows the equivalent distribution for a nonsense regression (case b in the table). The third panel (c, left in the lower row) is for the distribution of the t-test on the coefficient of x_t in a regression of y_t on x_t, y_{t-1} and x_{t-1} when the data are generated as unrelated stationary first-order autoregressive processes. The final panel (d) shows the t-test on the equilibrium-correction coefficient for data generated by a cointegrated process (see §12.10 below).

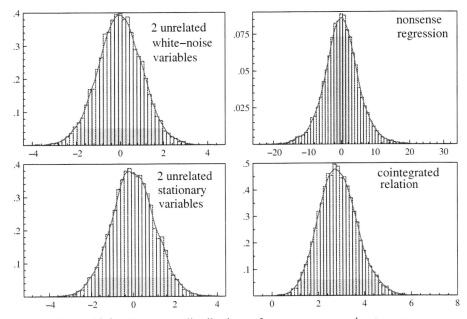

Figure 12.3 Frequency distributions of nonsense-regression t-tests.

The first and third panels are close to the actual distribution of Student's t; the former is as expected from statistical theory, whereas the latter shows that outcome is approximately correct in dynamic models once the dynamics have been included in the equation specification. The second panel shows an outcome that is wildly different from t, with a distributional spread so wide that most of the probability lies outside the usual region of ± 2. While the last distribution is not centered on zero – because the true relation is indeed non-null – it is included to show that the range of the distribution is roughly correct.

Thus, panels (c) and (d) show that, by themselves, neither dynamics nor unit-root non-stationarity induce serious distortions: the nonsense-regressions problem is due to incorrect model specification. Indeed, when y_{t-1} and x_{t-1} are added as regressors in case (b), the correct distribution results for $t_{\beta_1=0}$, delivering a panel very similar to (c), so the excess rejection is due to the wrong standard error being used in the denominator (which as shown above, is badly downwards biased by the untreated residual autocorrelation).

Almost all available software packages contain a regression routine that calculates coefficient estimates, t-values, and R^2 based on OLS. Since the computer will calculate the coefficients independently of whether the variables are stationary or not (and without issuing a warning when they are not) it is important to be aware of the following implications for regressions with unconnected non-stationary variables:

(i) Although $E[\widehat{\beta}_1] = 0$, nevertheless $t_{\beta_1=0}$ diverges to infinity as T increases, so that conventionally-calculated critical values are incorrect (see Hendry, 1995b, ch. 3).

(ii) R^2 cannot be interpreted as a measure of goodness-of-fit.

The first point means that one will too frequently reject the null hypothesis ($\beta_1 = 0$) when it is true. Even in the best case, when $\beta_1 \neq 0$, i.e., when y_t and x_t are causally related, standard t-tests will be biased with too frequent rejections of a null hypothesis such as $\beta_1 = 1$, when it is true. Hence statistical inference from regression models with non-stationary variables is unreliable based on standard OLS output.

All this points to the crucial importance of *always* checking the residuals of the empirical model for (unmodelled) residual autocorrelation. If autocorrelation is found, then the model should be re-specified to account for this feature, because many of the conventional statistical distributions, such as Student's t, the F, and the χ^2 distributions become approximately valid once the model is re-specified to have a white-noise error. So even though unit roots impart an important non-stationarity to the data, reformulating the model to have white-noise errors is a good step towards solving the problem.

12.9 Testing for unit roots

We have demonstrated that stochastic trends in the data are important for statistical inference. We will now discuss how to test for the presence of unit roots in the data. However, the distinction between a unit-root process and a near unit-root process need not be crucial for practical modeling. Even though a variable is stationary, but with a root close to unity (say, $\rho > 0.95$) it is often a good idea to act as if there are unit roots to obtain robust statistical inference.

We will now consider unit-root testing in a univariate setting. Consider estimating β in the autoregressive model:

$$y_t = \beta y_{t-1} + \epsilon_t \quad \text{where} \quad \epsilon_t \sim \text{IN} \left[0, \sigma_\epsilon^2\right] \tag{12.17}$$

under the null of $\beta = 1$ and $y_0 = 0$ (i.e., no deterministic trend in the levels), using a sample of size T. Because $\text{V}[y_t] = \sigma_\epsilon^2 t$, the data second moments (like $\sum_{t=1}^{T} y_{t-1}^2$) grow at order T^2, so the distribution of $\widehat{\beta} - \beta$ 'collapses' very quickly. Again, we can illustrate this by simulation, estimating (12.17) at $T = 25$, 100, 400, and 1000. The four panels for the estimated distribution in Figure 12.4 have been standardized to the same x-axis for visual comparison – and the convergence is dramatic. For comparison, the corresponding graphs for $\beta = 0.5$ are shown in Figure 12.5, where second moments grow at order T. Thus, to obtain a non-degenerate limiting distribution for $\widehat{\beta} - \beta$, scaling by T is required (rather than $\sqrt{T}$ for I(0) data). Moreover, even after that scaling, the form of the limiting distribution is different from that holding under stationarity.

The 't-statistic' for testing H_0: $\beta = 1$, often called the Dickey–Fuller test after Dickey and Fuller (1979), is easily computed, but does not have a standard t-distribution. Consequently, conventional critical values are incorrect, and using them

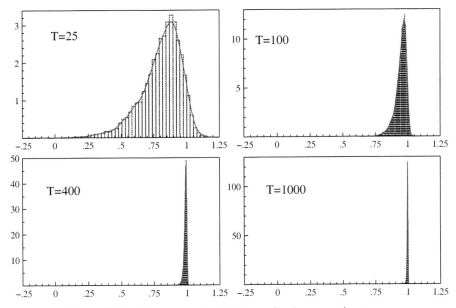

Figure 12.4   Frequency distributions of unit-root estimators.

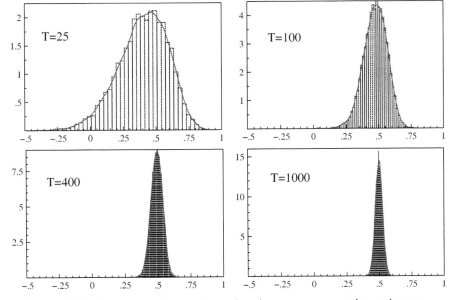

Figure 12.5   Frequency distributions of stationary autoregression estimators.

can lead to over-rejection of the null of a unit root when it is true. Rather, the Dickey–Fuller (*DF*) test has a skewed distribution with a long left tail, making it hard to discriminate the null of a unit root from alternatives close to unity. Unfortunately, the form of the limiting distribution of the *DF* test is also altered by the presence of a constant or a trend in either the DGP or the model. This means that different critical values are required in each case, although all the required tables of the correct critical values are available. Worse still, wrong choices of what deterministic terms to include – or which table is applicable – can seriously distort inference. The role and the interpretation of the constant term and the trend in the model changes as we move from the stationary case to the non-stationary unit-root case. It is also the case for stationary data that incorrectly omitting (say) an intercept can be disastrous, but mistakes are more easily made when the data are non-stationary. However, always including a constant and a trend in the estimated model ensures that the test will have the correct rejection frequency under the null for most economic time series. The required critical values have been tabulated using Monte Carlo simulations by Dickey and Fuller (1979, 1981), and most time-series econometric software (e.g., PcGive, Hendry and Doornik, 2001) automatically provides the correct critical values for unit-root tests in almost all relevant cases.

12.10 Testing for cointegration

When data are non-stationary purely due to unit roots, they can be brought back to stationarity by linear transformations, for example, by differencing, as in $x_t - x_{t-1}$. If $x_t \sim I(1)$, then by definition $\Delta x_t \sim I(0)$. An alternative is to try a linear transformation $y_t - \beta x_t$, which induces cointegration when $y_t - \beta x_t \sim I(0)$, but unlike differencing, there is no guarantee that $y_t - \beta x_t$ is $I(0)$ for any value of β.

There are many possible tests for cointegration: the most general of them is the multivariate test based on the vector autoregressive representation (VAR) discussed in Johansen (1988). Here we first consider tests based on the static and the dynamic regression model, assuming that x_t can be treated as weakly exogenous for the parameters of the conditional model (see e.g., Engle, Hendry and Richard, 1983; see §12.11 for when it does not hold).[2] The condition that there exists a genuine causal link between y_t and x_t is that the residual $u_t \sim I(0)$, otherwise a 'nonsense regression' has been estimated. Therefore, the Engle–Granger test procedure (Engle and Granger, 1987) is based on testing that the residuals u_t from a static regression model are stationary. As discussed in the previous section, the test of the null of a unit coefficient, using the *DF* test, implies using a non-standard distribution.

Let $\widehat{u}_t = y_t - \widehat{\beta} x_t$ where $\widehat{\beta}$ is the OLS estimate of the long-run parameter β, then the null hypothesis of the *DF* test is H_0: $\rho = 1$, or equivalently, H_0: $1 - \rho = 0$ in:

$$\widehat{u}_t = \rho \widehat{u}_{t-1} + \varepsilon_t \tag{12.18}$$

---

[2]Regression methods can be applied to model I(1) variables which are in fact linked (i.e., cointegrated). Most tests still have conventional distributions, apart from that corresponding to a test for a unit root.

or:

$$\Delta\widehat{u}_t = (1 - \rho)\widehat{u}_{t-1} + \varepsilon_t.$$

The test is based on the assumption that ε_t in (12.18) is white noise, and if the AR(1) model in (12.18) does not deliver white-noise errors, then it has to be augmented by lagged differences of residuals:

$$\Delta\widehat{u}_t = (1 - \rho)\widehat{u}_{t-1} + \psi_1\Delta\widehat{u}_{t-1} + \cdots + \psi_m\Delta\widehat{u}_{t-m} + \varepsilon_t. \tag{12.19}$$

We call the test of H_0: $1 - \rho = 0$ in (12.19) the augmented Dickey–Fuller test (*ADF*). See MacKinnon (1991), for response surface approximations from which accurate critical values can be obtained. A drawback of the *DF*-type test procedure (see Campos, Ericsson and Hendry, 1996, for a discussion of this drawback) is that the autoregressive model (12.18) for $\widehat{u}_t$ is the equivalent of imposing a common dynamic factor on the static regression model:

$$(1 - \rho L)y_t = \beta_0(1 - \rho) + \beta_1(1 - \rho L)x_t + \varepsilon_t. \tag{12.20}$$

For the *DF* test to have high power to reject H_0: $1 - \rho = 0$ when it is false, the common-factor restriction in (12.20) should be data consistent. Empirical evidence has not produced much support for such common factors, rendering such tests non-optimal. Instead, Kremers, Ericsson and Dolado (1992) contrast them with a direct test for H_0: $\alpha_2 = 0$ in:

$$\Delta y_t = \alpha_0 + \alpha_1\Delta x_t + \alpha_2(y_{t-1} - \beta_1 x_{t-1}) + \varepsilon_t, \tag{12.21}$$

where the parameters $\{\alpha_0, \alpha_1, \alpha_2, \beta_1\}$ are not constrained by the common-factor restriction in (12.20).

Unfortunately, the null rejection frequency of their test depends on the values of the 'nuisance' parameters α_1 and σ_ε^2, so Kiviet and Phillips (1992) developed a test which is invariant to these values. In this improved test x_{t-1} enters unrestrictedly, so it involves testing H_0: $\alpha_2 = 0$ in:

$$\Delta y_t = \alpha_0 + \alpha_1\Delta x_t + \alpha_2 y_{t-1} + \delta_1 x_{t-1} + \varepsilon_t, \tag{12.22}$$

where there are no further restrictions imposed on the parameters. This test first appeared in PcGive in the early 1980s, and is therefore called the *PcGive unit-root test*. Model (12.22) is in error correction (or better: equilibrium correction) form, and the test is also called *error correction* test (or ECM test). Ericsson and MacKinnon (1999) provide critical values based on response surfaces.

The distribution of the PcGive unit-root test is illustrated in Fig. 12.3, panel d. Although non-standard, so its critical values have been separately tabulated, its distribution is much closer to the Student t-distribution than the Dickey–Fuller, and correspondingly Banerjee, Dolado, Galbraith and Hendry (1993) find the power of $t_{\alpha_2=0}$ can be high relative to the *DF* test. However, when x_t is not weakly exogenous (i.e., when not only y_t adjusts to the previous equilibrium error as in (12.21), but also x_t does), the test is potentially a poor way of detecting cointegration. In this case, a multivariate test procedure is needed.

12.11 Invalid weak exogeneity in a cointegration equation

The final example in this section considers (12.21) when $\beta_1 = 1$ and weak exogeneity does not hold:

$$\Delta y_t = \alpha_1 \Delta x_t + \alpha_2 (y_{t-1} - x_{t-1}) + \epsilon_{1,t} \tag{12.23}$$

where:

$$\Delta x_t = \alpha_3 (y_{t-1} - x_{t-1}) + \epsilon_{2,t} \tag{12.24}$$

when $E[\epsilon_{i,t}^2] = 1$ and $E[\epsilon_{i,t}\epsilon_{j,s}] = 0 \; \forall t, s$ with $i, j = 1, 2$, but $i, t \neq j, s$. The estimated equation is (12.23), and the issue of concern is that the same cointegration vector $(y_{t-1} - x_{t-1})$ enters both equations, thus violating weak exogeneity (as defined in Engle, Hendry and Richard, 1983). Both $\{y_t\}$ and $\{x_t\}$ are individually I(1), so that they need differencing precisely once to become stationary.

To implement the DGP, it is convenient to write (12.23)–(12.24) as:

$$\begin{pmatrix} 1 & -\alpha_1 \\ 0 & 1 \end{pmatrix} \begin{pmatrix} \Delta y_t \\ \Delta x_t \end{pmatrix} = \begin{pmatrix} \alpha_2 \\ \alpha_3 \end{pmatrix} \begin{pmatrix} 1 & -1 \end{pmatrix} \begin{pmatrix} y_{t-1} \\ x_{t-1} \end{pmatrix} + \epsilon_t, \quad \epsilon_t \sim N[\mathbf{0}, \mathbf{I}_2].$$

Pre-multiplying by

$$\begin{pmatrix} 1 & -\alpha_1 \\ 0 & 1 \end{pmatrix}^{-1} = \begin{pmatrix} 1 & \alpha_1 \\ 0 & 1 \end{pmatrix}$$

leads to

$$\begin{pmatrix} \Delta y_t \\ \Delta x_t \end{pmatrix} = \begin{pmatrix} \alpha_2 + \alpha_1\alpha_3 \\ \alpha_3 \end{pmatrix} \begin{pmatrix} 1 & -1 \end{pmatrix} \begin{pmatrix} y_t \\ x_t \end{pmatrix} + \nu_t, \quad \nu_t \sim N[\mathbf{0}, \Sigma],$$

$$\Sigma = \begin{pmatrix} 1 + \alpha_1^2 & \alpha_1 \\ \alpha_1 & 1 \end{pmatrix}.$$

The Monte Carlo uses $\alpha_1 = 0.5, \alpha_2 = -0.1, \alpha_3 = 0.2$ and $T = 60, M = 1000$, yielding the following results:

	Mean	Bias	MCSE	MCSD	ESE
α_1	0.496	−0.004	0.0042	0.131	0.132
α_2	−0.120	−0.020	0.0025	0.080	0.078
$\tilde{\sigma}^2$	1.004			0.182	

Thus, despite the violation of weak exogeneity, only a small bias appears in the coefficients of I(0) regressors. As discussed in Hendry (1995c), however, the impact on inference about the true value of parameters of I(1) variables can be marked.

Chapter 13

Advanced econometrics

The topics noted in this final section are some of the authors' present research interests, and assume a willingness on the part of students to undertake independent study to follow up relevant issues.

13.1 The role of asymptotic distribution theory in Monte Carlo

Chapter 16 focuses on asymptotics, the evaluation of population characteristics of linear models, and local asymptotic power functions in stationary processes, and Chapter 14 notes the close links between control variates and limiting distributions. However, as yet little has been done to link limiting distributions with Monte Carlo outcomes in integrated processes and this topic deserves greater study (see inter alia, Gonzalo, 1989, Johansen, 1988, Phillips, 1987a, 1987b, Phillips and Loretan, 1991, Banerjee, Dolado, Galbraith and Hendry, 1993, Doornik, Hendry and Nielsen, 1998 and Doornik, 1998 for some recent results).

13.2 Distributions of inconsistent estimators

Most practical studies involve models which are unknowingly mis-specified in various ways. Monte Carlo allows any given combinations of specification mistakes to be studied, but again general yet usable results are needed to guide empirical research. For examples, see Hendry (1979a, 1982), Maasoumi and Phillips (1982), White (1990), and Domowitz and White (1982). How helpful is orthogonalization of the variables? How do mis-specifications and non-stationarities of various forms interact?

117

13.3 The impacts of structural breaks on econometric modelling

Many regime shifts have occurred during the post-war period, perturbing what were apparently well-established relationships. How powerful are tests for detecting such effects? Can we distinguish between breaks within a relationship, and induced changes due to breaks elsewhere in the economy interacting with mis-specification (see Hendry, 1979b)? How different are stationary and I(1) but cointegrated systems in their responses to both kinds of shift? For some examples see Perron (1989), Hendry and Neale (1991), and Hendry and Doornik (1997), and Hendry (2000).

13.4 Testing the Lucas critique

This topic is of course intimately related to the previous one, but focuses on invariance to shifts, and super exogeneity, rather than non-constancy. Can we detect the potential presence of the Lucas (1974) critique (a problem actually raised by many previous writers including Frisch, 1938, and Haavelmo, 1944: see Aldrich, 1989, and Hendry and Morgan, 1995), and if so, how powerful are tests thereof (see Engle and Hendry, 1993, Ericsson and Irons, 1995)? Is the Lucas critique potentially refutable for models involving expectations (see Hendry, 1988, and Favero and Hendry, 1992), or are the powers of conventional tests for consequential changes in marginal processes simply too low? If so, why do so many conditional empirical models suffer easily detected predictive failures? Does the type of break matter, namely in dynamics, in deterministic terms such as intercepts, or in error variances (for an argument that mainly deterministic shifts matter, see Hendry, 1997). For a recent analysis see Hendry and Mizon (2000).

13.5 Encompassing and non-nested hypothesis tests

As yet we know surprisingly little about the finite-sample powers of encompassing tests (although see Pesaran, 1974, and Ericsson, 1986: Hendry and Richard, 1989, provide a survey). This is especially true when other complications are introduced such as various forms of non-stationarity. The Monte Carlo in Govaerts, Hendry and Richard (1994) shows important differences between various forms of encompassing test.

13.6 Non-existence of moments

This issue, considered in detail here, concerns the behaviour of Monte Carlo estimation of simulation moments when the relevant theoretical moments do not exist (see Sargan, 1982). The rth moment of a statistic, or of a random variable Z, with density function

$f_Z(z)$, is defined by:

$$E[Z^r] = \int_{-\infty}^{\infty} z^r f_Z(z) dz,$$ (13.1)

when it exists. Because this integral involves powers of Z, unless $f_Z(z)$ 'dies out' sufficiently rapidly in the tails, the integral may not converge, in which case the relevant moment will not exist. The empirical counterpart of non-existence of a given moment is 'wild' behaviour in estimates of it from observables. This poses an interesting issue for Monte Carlo studies that focus on estimating moments: what happens when the corresponding theoretical moment does not exist?

We consider two causes of non-existent moments: (1) the error distribution generating the Monte Carlo data has no moments (§13.6.1); (2) the estimator has no moments although the error process has (§13.6.2) The simplest example of §13.6.1 is a Cauchy distribution, which is also a $t(1)$. The simplest example of §13.6.2 is a just-identified IV estimator. We will discuss these two simple cases in turn as they serve to highlight the main problems likely to arise.

13.6.1 The Cauchy distribution

The formula for $f_Z(z)$ when Z is a Cauchy variate is:

$$f_Z(z) = \pi^{-1} \left(1 + z^2\right)^{-1},$$ (13.2)

where $\pi = 3.141592\ldots$ This distribution is symmetric about the origin (so has a median of zero), and the upper and lower quartiles are ± 1, yet it has no integral moments of order unity (or higher). Approximately 1% of the mass lies outside ± 4. An excellent source of information is Johnson, Kotz and Balakrishnan (1994).

For our present purposes, one of the more interesting phenomena of the Cauchy is that the mean of any sample size from (13.2) has the same distribution as a single observation. This issue is investigated by creating an experiment to generate a variate as a constant plus a Cauchy error, then regressing the variate on the constant at every feasible sample size. We use the $t(1)$ to generate a Cauchy in PcNaive, and a plot of the histogram and estimated density (here for $M = 1000$ sample means of size $T = 50$) looks rather odd, see Figure 13.1a, with most of the mass in a small central interval, but some scattered over an enormous range, by drawing 1000 single observations, it is easily verified that the graphs have the same shape (note that discarding observations outside a certain range ensures a bounded range and hence has the paradoxical implication that the moments do exist).

In fact, there is a marked contrast when the first moment, at least, exists as it does with a $t(2)$. Clearly, the outcome is much less wild, despite the non-existence of second and higher moments.

The other aspect of concern is the outcome of recursive procedures when no moments exist. The outcome is shown in Figure 13.1b, and again reveals wild behaviour,

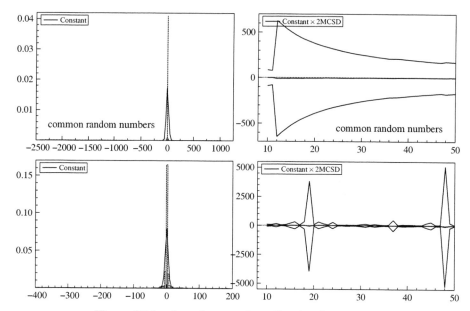

Figure 13.1   Sample mean from Cauchy distribution.

particularly when not using common random numbers: the MCSD (which itself is estimating a non-existent moment) is > 1000 on some occasions, and is quite unrelated to the ESE. It is fun to see how the histogram jumps around when running the experiment without common random numbers. Although the sample means all seem to be closely centered on zero (as might be expected by the median unbiased property), this is an illusion created by the immense range of the graph units. Also note that the ESE is essentially a straight line at all sample sizes and does not fall at the rate $1/\sqrt{T}$. The basic problem is that there is a high probability of extreme outliers, making the results very unreliable. Conversely, we could easily detect that, and there are many non-parametric statistics that remain valid in this setting.

13.6.2 No moments in an instrumental variables estimator

The focus here is closely related, yet differs in important ways. Now the error process will be normal, so all of its moments exist, and the econometric equation of interest will be the linear model:

$$y_t = x_t\beta + \epsilon_t \quad \text{where} \quad \epsilon_t \sim \text{IN}\,[0,1]\,, \tag{13.3}$$

for $t = 1,\ldots,T$. However, $\text{E}[x_t\epsilon_t] \neq 0$, due to simultaneity perhaps, but there exists a marginal model for x_t as a function of a variable z_t which is weakly exogenous for β:

$$x_t = z_t\gamma + u_t \quad \text{where} \quad u_t \sim \text{IN}\,\left[0, \sigma_u^2\right]\,, \tag{13.4}$$

and $E[z_t u_t] = E[z_t \epsilon_t] = 0$. We set $\sigma_u^2 = 1$ (check whether this involves any loss of generality in a linear system), and assumed that $\{z_t\}$ is generated by a first-order autoregressive process, so is in fact strongly exogenous.

From (13.4), OLS estimation of γ conditional on $\{z_t\}$ yields:

$$\widehat{\gamma} \sim N\left[\gamma, v\right] \quad \text{where } v = \sigma_u^2 \left(\sum_{t=1}^{T} z_t^2\right)^{-1}. \tag{13.5}$$

Thus, IV estimation of β from (13.3) produces:

$$\widehat{\beta} = \beta + \left(\sum_{t=1}^{T} z_t x_t\right)^{-1} \sum_{t=1}^{T} z_t \epsilon_t = \beta + \widehat{\gamma}^{-1}\left(\sum_{t=1}^{T} z_t^2\right)^{-1} \sum_{t=1}^{T} z_t \epsilon_t. \tag{13.6}$$

The problem for IV is clear from the last term in (13.6): if $\widehat{\gamma}$ has a high probability of lying in a neighbourhood of zero (denoted $\mathcal{N}_0$), then wild estimates of β will result. Technically, due to assuming normality in the error processes, no moments of $\widehat{\beta}$ exist whatever $P(\widehat{\gamma} \in \mathcal{N}_0) \neq 0$, but in practice the problem may be more or less apparent. To illustrate, consider the two polar cases $\gamma = 0.1$ and $\gamma = 4.0$ when $v = 0.1$. If we define $\mathcal{N}_0$ as $[-0.1, 0.1]$, then in the former case:

$$P\left(\widehat{\gamma} \in \mathcal{N}_0\right) = P\left(|\widehat{\gamma}| \leq 0.1\right) = P\left(-0.2 \leq (\widehat{\gamma} - \gamma) \leq 0.0\right) \approx 0.47. \tag{13.7}$$

The corresponding probability is very small in the second case.

In Monte Carlo terms, in the first case we are likely to draw a sample with $\widehat{\gamma}$ near zero, and so 'observe' the non-existence, whereas in the latter case, for a conventional number of replications (100 to 1000, say) we are unlikely to draw any extreme outliers. Figure 13.2a shows the extremely erratic behaviour of IV when (13.7) holds, so that OLS outcomes are dwarfed (here with $z_t \sim N[0, 0.1]$, $\beta = 1$, $\gamma = 0.1$), whereas the larger $\gamma = 4$ simulations seem fine in Figure 13.2c despite the theoretical non-existence of the moments being estimated.

Indeed, when $\gamma = 4$, the ESE and MCSD are close at all sample sizes. The histograms and density functions of the IV coefficient estimates at $T = 40$ would confirm this difference due to changing γ, although the t-distributions are well behaved in both cases (Fig. 13.2b,d). Throughout, OLS is well behaved. The analysis in Sargan (1982) explains such outcomes in terms of Monte Carlo estimating the moments of Nagar approximations (see Nagar, 1959), and serves as a final emphasis on the advantages of closely linking theory and simulation. Also see the analysis in Phillips (1989).

13.7 Cointegration analysis

System cointegration analysis commences from a closed, linear dynamic system for n variables $\mathbf{x}_t$, with a maximum lag length of s periods, and assume normality, thereby

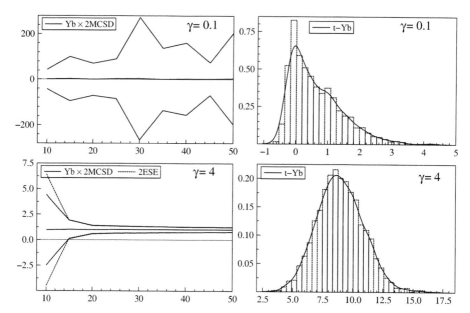

Figure 13.2   No moments in an IV estimator, $\gamma = 0.1$ (top), $\gamma = 4$ (bottom).

postulating a vector autoregression (VAR) with m deterministic variables $\mathbf{q}_t$, over a sample $t = 1, \ldots, T$, expressed as:

$$\Delta \mathbf{y}_t = \sum_{j=1}^{s-1} \delta_j \Delta \mathbf{y}_{t-j} + \mathbf{P}_0 \mathbf{y}_{t-1} + \mathbf{\Phi} \mathbf{q}_t + \nu_t \text{ where } \nu_t \sim \mathsf{IN}_n \left[\mathbf{0}, \mathbf{\Omega} \right], \qquad (13.8)$$

when $\mathsf{IN}_n \left[\mathbf{0}, \mathbf{\Omega} \right]$ denotes an n-dimensional independent, normal density with mean zero and covariance matrix $\mathbf{\Omega}$ (symmetric, positive definite). In (13.8), the parameters $(\delta_1 \ldots \delta_{s-1}, \mathbf{P}_0, \mathbf{\Phi}, \mathbf{\Omega})$ are assumed to be constant and variation free, with sufficient observations to sustain estimation and inference $(T - s \gg n(s + m + 2))$. To allow interpretation of the results, none of the roots of the companion-form polynomial should lie inside the unit circle (see e.g., Chapter 16 and Banerjee, Dolado, Galbraith and Hendry, 1993, Ch. 5). Note that (13.8) is isomorphic to a VAR in levels, which is the format for estimation:

$$\mathbf{y}_t = \sum_{j=1}^{s} \pi_j \mathbf{y}_{t-j} + \mathbf{\Phi} \mathbf{q}_t + \nu_t \text{ where } \nu_t \sim \mathsf{IN}_n \left[\mathbf{0}, \mathbf{\Omega} \right].$$

Equation (13.8) shows that the matrix $\mathbf{P}_0$ determines how the levels of the process $\mathbf{y}$ enter the system: for example, when $\mathbf{P}_0 = \mathbf{0}$, the dynamic evolution does not depend on the levels. This indicates the importance of the rank of $\mathbf{P}_0$ in the analysis. The statistical hypothesis of cointegration (assuming that I(2)-ness is ruled out) is:

$$\mathsf{H}(p): \text{ rank } (\mathbf{P}_0) \leq p.$$

Under this hypothesis, $\mathbf{P}_0$ can be written as the product of two matrices:

$$\mathbf{P}_0 = \alpha\beta',$$

where α and β have dimension $n \times p$, and vary freely. As suggested by Johansen (1988, 1995), such a restriction can be analyzed by maximum likelihood methods. PcNaive allows simulation of this procedure, and was, for example, used for that purpose in Doornik, Hendry and Nielsen (1998), also see §7.6, and Doornik and Hendry (2001b).

In addition to those examples just noted, many other topics can be studied at the research level using PcNaive, despite its equally obvious limitation to 'conventional' inference problems. In many instances, conducting a simulation study of a mimic of the empirical model would yield valuable insights into what inferences are likely to be credible and what rest more on hope than reality.

Part IV

Monte Carlo Theory

Chapter 14

Monte Carlo Methods

14.1 Stochastic solutions to deterministic problems

Monte Carlo is a method for solving deterministic (i.e., mathematical) problems by solving a stochastic problem which has the same solution. At first encounter, that idea seems odd and raises two questions: 'why adopt such a circuitous route?', and 'how do we know in advance that the exact and stochastic problems will have the same answer?' An illustration should help clarify the answers. Consider calculating:

$$\int_a^b x e^{-\frac{1}{2}x^2} \, dx. \tag{14.1}$$

This integral is not straightforward to evaluate analytically. However, the integral corresponds to the mean value over the interval $[a, b]$ of a random variable X distributed as $\sqrt{(2\pi)}$ times the standard normal density. If random numbers from $\mathsf{IN}[0,1]$ can be created on a computer, their mean over $[a, b]$ can be calculated numerically, solving the integration problem (on scaling by $\sqrt{2\pi}$).

To apply Monte Carlo to a given problem, one must be able to prove in advance that the stochastic problem has the same solution as the analytical one, which fortunately is often easy to do, as will transpire to be the case for the wide class of distribution sampling methods discussed in §14.2. This ease of relating deterministic and stochastic problems will then extend directly to the more sophisticated simulation techniques described in §14.3. In practice, Monte Carlo is less indirect than the above may suggest, in that the corresponding analytical problem is usually solved as far as feasible, and only any intractable remainder is obtained numerically.

One important cost of tackling an analytical problem numerically is that the result is specific to the range of numerical values obtained, as with a given choice of $[a, b]$ in (14.1), rather than an analytical formula which can be widely applied. Three techniques help circumvent this drawback, namely embedding the problem to be solved in a suitably general setting, adopting a comprehensive experimental design to cover the range of likely values of interest, and appropriately summarizing the experimental findings in numerical-analytical formulae based on response functions estimated from the entire set of experiments conducted. An important step towards achieving adequate generality is to establish whether there are any features of the problem to which the solution is invariant, in which case the solution obtained applies to all members of the invariance class.

A second, and equally serious, cost of using a stochastic numerical approach is that the results are also imprecise, and different results could be obtained for the same problem in a repeated calculation if a different starting seed is used. To an extent, this is an inherent cost of Monte Carlo in many settings, but we will also investigate clever devices which solve the same desired analytical problem in different numerical ways, some of which are dramatically more precise for a given effort expended than others.

We consider the pure simulation approach in §14.2 and more sophisticated Monte Carlo techniques for improving precision in §14.3. In §14.4 we note the importance of invariance arguments. §14.5 describes the role of asymptotic analysis in Monte Carlo studies of stationary processes. Then we investigate recursive Monte Carlo techniques in §14.6, as these are of considerable relevance to econometric research, because they focus efficiently on how the finite-sample behaviour of estimators and tests varies as the sample size changes. The chapter concludes in §14.7 with some comments on experimental design, followed by discussions of response surface methods for analyzing experimental results in §14.8.

Good general references on Monte Carlo methods are Hammersley and Handscomb (1964), Kleijnen (1974), Sobol' (1974), Kennedy and Gentle (1980) and Ripley (1987); Hendry (1984), Davidson and MacKinnon (1993) and Ericsson and Marquez (1998) provide analyses of its role in econometrics.[1]

14.2 Distribution sampling

In econometrics, Monte Carlo is primarily used as a device to investigate the behaviour in finite samples of various statistics of interest (estimators, standard errors, tests etc.). A Monte Carlo experiment therefore typically involves directly mimicking on a computer the desired data generation process (DGP) for the type of system and data to which the statistical methods are to be applied, although Monte Carlo experiments were in fact conducted manually long before computers were invented. The artificial DGP to be used in the experiment should reflect all relevant aspects of the economy, in order to produce data that are applicable to the real world econometric problem under study.

---

[1]Conducting classroom simulations as a didactic device is long established: for example, Hammersley and Handscomb, 1964, p.7 report a case from early this century in which students of statistics poured lead-shot down boards studded with pins, that deflected the shot to be collected in a series of boxes at the bottom of the board, to see if the quantity of shot in each box matched the theoretical statistical prediction. At this point, however, the analogy breaks down, since the students' exercise was labour intensive whilst present methods are capital intensive!

A clear distinction must be maintained throughout between the econometric model of that DGP (whose properties we wish to investigate) and the Monte Carlo model (which is used to study the econometric procedures). Statistical expectations with respect to the random variables in the econometric model and DGP will be denoted by E, so that if Y_t is a random variable with mean β from the DGP, then $\mathsf{E}[Y_t] = \beta$. Econometric estimators will usually be denoted by a^ (e.g., $\widehat{\beta}$).

For a given and fixed numerical choice of the parameters determining the DGP, a random sample of size T on the variables in the model is then drawn from that DGP, and the modelling methods and/or statistics of interest are calculated from the resulting sample of artificial data. A Monte Carlo experiment involves repeating this process many times (M say) in order to create a large Monte Carlo sample on the behaviour of the relevant statistics, where M is called the number of replications or the Monte Carlo sample size. The empirical distributions of the statistics based on the artificial data then simulate the actual, but unknown, theoretical distributions which we seek. This particular approach is termed distribution sampling, and was used (e.g.) by Student (1908) to check his hypothesized distribution for the t-statistic.

The following statistical theorem underlies most Monte Carlo finite-sample studies in econometrics and is applicable when the Monte Carlo sample size M is large. Let:

$$x_i \sim \mathsf{IID}(\mu, \sigma^2),$$

where $\mathsf{IID}(\mu, \sigma^2)$ denotes an *Identical, Independent* sample drawn from a *Distribution* with finite mean μ and finite variance $\sigma^2 > 0$ (which remain the same for all i). However, while we can observe the $\{x_i\}$, the form of the distribution $\mathsf{D}(\cdot)$, and both μ and σ^2 are unknown. The objective of the Monte Carlo is to estimate these unknowns. Let $\mathcal{E}$ denote an expectation with respect to the random variables in the Monte Carlo (to distinguish from E in the econometric model), and denote Monte Carlo estimators by ~ (as well as ‾ for means e.g., $\overline{x}$). Finally, let:

$$\widetilde{x} = \overline{x} = M^{-1} \sum_{i=1}^{M} x_i \tag{14.2}$$

then:

$$\mathcal{E}\left[\overline{x}\right] = \mu, \tag{14.3}$$

and:

$$\mathcal{E}\left[(\overline{x} - \mu)^2\right] = \mathcal{V}\left[\overline{x}\right] = \sigma^2/M, \tag{14.4}$$

where $\mathcal{V}[\cdot]$ denotes the variance with respect to the random variables in the Monte Carlo. Also:

$$\overline{x} \underset{M \to \infty}{\frown} \mathsf{N}\left[\mu, \sigma^2/M\right], \tag{14.5}$$

where $\mathsf{N}[\mu, \sigma^2/M]$ denotes a Normal distribution with mean μ and variance σ^2/M. The result in (14.5) is only approximate for finite M, but can itself be investigated using Monte Carlo. Further, if:

$$\tilde{\sigma}^2 = (M-1)^{-1} \sum_{i=1}^{M} (x_i - \overline{x})^2, \tag{14.6}$$

then:

$$\mathcal{E}\left[\tilde{\sigma}^2\right] = \sigma^2 \tag{14.7}$$

and so:

$$\mathcal{E}\left[\tilde{\sigma}^2/M\right] = \sigma^2/M = \mathcal{V}\left[\overline{x}\right]. \tag{14.8}$$

Thus, from (14.3), the Monte Carlo sample mean $\overline{x}$ of a set of IID drawings from a population with mean μ is an unbiased estimator of μ, and from (14.4), $\overline{x}$ has a variance of σ^2/M. Further, from (14.5), $\overline{x}$ is normally distributed around μ when M is large. This finding establishes that we can unbiasedly estimate the unknown value of μ using $\overline{x}$, with a variance that can be made as small as desired by increasing M.

Next, from (14.7), the sample variance $\tilde{\sigma}^2$ defined in (14.6) is an unbiased estimator of the unknown population variance, and when divided by the sample size, delivers an unbiased estimator of the variance of the sample mean around μ as seen in (14.8). Thus, we can also calculate measures of the uncertainty in the experiment. From (14.4), $\mathcal{V}\left[\overline{x}\right]$ tends to zero as $M \rightarrow \infty$, and we can check on this by computing (14.8) at ever larger M. Also, $\overline{x}$ and $\tilde{\sigma}^2$ tend to their population counterparts, and from (14.5), we can test hypotheses about μ, and about σ^2 by using the approximate χ^2 distribution corresponding to assuming (14.5) holds in (14.6).

While it is not entailed by the above theorem, histograms and estimated density functions provide empirical analogues of theoretical density functions, and so can help to describe the distributional shape (see, e.g., Silverman, 1986).

The basic theorem only requires elementary principles for its proof, together with a Central Limit Theorem if convergence to normality is needed (see, e.g., Hendry, 1995b). To apply the basic theorem to estimate the theoretical moments of any desired distribution using the moments of artificial samples, we must be able to generate $\{x_i\}$ with the requisite properties *despite the fact that* D($\cdot$), μ *and* σ^2 *are unknown*. The trick in Monte Carlo is to design experiments such that the basic theorem applies despite the complexity of the statistical process or the methods to be investigated. Create a numerical representation of the relevant DGP which generates data on a set of n random variables $\{Y_{j,t}\} = (Y_{1,1}, \ldots, Y_{n,T})$, whose distribution is therefore known: examples include VARs, cointegrated systems etc. The econometric problem involves studying the properties of (complicated) functions of the form:

$$g\left[h_1\left(\{Y_{j,t}\}\right), \ldots, h_k\left(\{Y_{j,t}\}\right)\right].$$

Such functions might include regression coefficients, their standard errors, t-statistics, diagnostic tests and so on. We wish to study their expectations or distributions etc., in settings where that is not analytically tractable. To achieve that goal, we use the basic theorem above. First, generate the $\{x_i\}$ from the random variables $\{Y_{j,t}\}$ simply by computing:

$$x_i = g\left[h_1\left(\{Y_{j,t}\}\right), \ldots, h_k\left(\{Y_{j,t}\}\right)\right]. \tag{14.9}$$

In (14.9), the indices are $i = 1, \ldots, M$ replications of the experiment in each of which we generate $j = 1, \ldots, n$ different random variables from the DGP at each of $t = 1, \ldots, T$ observations. The DGP and $g(\cdot)$ are the 'econometric model', whereas the 'Monte Carlo model' is (here) simply simulating the behaviour of the functions $g(\cdot)$ by using random numbers from the appropriate distributions in place of random variables. Since the DGP is fully specified numerically, it must generate $\{Y_{j,t}\}$ with the appropriate properties. When the econometric analysis is correct, the $g(\cdot)$ are the appropriate functions to calculate. Although $\mathsf{E}\left[g\left(\cdot\right)\right] = \mu$ may be impossible to derive, we can estimate it by $\overline{x}$ from (14.9).

Since the Monte Carlo artificial DGP for the $\{Y_{j,t}\}$ mimics that for the analytic problem:

$$\mathcal{E}[\overline{x}] = \mathsf{E}\left[g\left[h_1\left(\{Y_{j,t}\}\right), \ldots, h_k\left(\{Y_{j,t}\}\right)\right]\right] = \mu. \tag{14.10}$$

Thus, by simulating the distribution of the $\{x_i\}$ artificially, we can estimate the properties of the unknown distribution of $g(\cdot)$ using (14.2)–(14.8) above. It is an inherent property of this mode of Monte Carlo that the stochastic problem always has the same solution as the deterministic problem which we really wish to solve.

Example $\mathsf{IN}[\mu, \sigma^2]$ process

To illustrate the use of Monte Carlo methods to solve distributional problems, consider analyzing an example involving a scalar random variable denoted by $Y_t \sim \mathsf{IID}(\mu, \sigma^2)$ so $\mathsf{E}[Y_t] = \mu$. We are interested in the properties of the mean $\overline{y}$ of a random sample $(y_1 \ldots y_T)$ as an estimator of the unknown μ, assuming its properties are not yet known (this example is also used in tutorial Chapter 4):

$$\overline{y} = T^{-1} \sum_{t=1}^{T} y_t. \tag{14.11}$$

In (14.11), $\overline{y}$ is the econometric estimator of interest. To simulate the DGP, write:

$$y_t = \mu + \epsilon_t \quad \text{with} \quad \epsilon_t \sim \mathsf{IN}\left[0, 1\right] \quad \text{where} \quad \mu \in (-\infty, \infty) \tag{14.12}$$

and $t = 1, \ldots, T$. Then (14.12) defines the DGP, which is a function of μ with parameter space given by the whole real line $\mathbb{R}$, and more generally denoted by $\boldsymbol{\Psi} = \{\psi : \psi \in \boldsymbol{\Psi}\}$. The specificity of the experiment above is determined by the range of values of μ actually considered (but this can be circumvented as shown below), by setting $\sigma^2 = 1$ (which is actually without loss of generality since we can always change the units of y and μ), by the selection of a normal density (which may or may not matter depending on the size of T, and the relevance of a central limit theorem to the problem on hand), and by the range of values of T considered. Consequently, if we draw a large sample from (14.12), its mean will reveal μ, although we prove this more formally below.

Because of its importance to finite-sample behaviour, we will define T to be a parameter of the Monte Carlo experiment (technically called a design variable) with a parameter space denoted by $\mathcal{T} = \{T : T \in \mathcal{T}\}$. The investigator as 'experimenter' must know the value of ψ to generate data, but as 'econometrician', is regarded as only observing the samples of data generated. This schizophrenia is essential if we are to mimic the practical econometric problem correctly, where 'nature' or 'society' may be deemed to be the experimenter and 'knows' the DGP, whereas a human is the econometrician, and does not! The complete parameter space of the design is given by $\boldsymbol{\Psi} \times \mathcal{T}$.

Example IN$[\mu, \sigma^2]$ process *(continued)*

To proceed, choose a particular value for the parameter μ, say $\mu = 6$, and for the sample size T, such as $T = 50$. If only one experiment is conducted, the results are specific to the parameter values chosen, but experiments can be conducted at a range of parameter values in the relevant parameter space. We can often establish the generality of results via invariance arguments, which prove that the outcome for one experiment will be replicated at all other values of the relevant parameter in the admissible parameter space and we will return to that issue in §14.4.

Next, generate a set of $\{y_t\}$ from (14.12) using random numbers to simulate the random variables $\{\epsilon_t\}$ and draw a sample of size 50, denoted by $(y_1, \ldots, y_{50})$. Calculate the Monte Carlo sample mean $\bar{y}$, and denote the outcome on the first replication or trial by $x_1 = \bar{y}$, which is a function of $(y_1 \ldots y_{50})$ and hence of $(\epsilon_1 \ldots \epsilon_{50})$:

$$x_1 = x_1 \left(\epsilon_1 \ldots \epsilon_{50}\right). \tag{14.13}$$

Now independently repeat this whole process M times (10 000 say), to generate a random sample of xs each of which is based on the mean of 50 ys:

$$\left(x_1 \ldots x_{10\,000}\right).$$

This collection of M trials at one point in the parameter space is called an experiment. For the DGP (14.12), we happen to know that the distribution of $\{x_i\}$ should be N$[6, 1/50]$, but in general we only know that the properties of $\{x_i\}$ derive from those of $\{y_t\}$ via the functions $g(\cdot)$. For the present example from (14.12):

$$\mathcal{E}[x_i] = \mathsf{E}[\bar{y}] = \mu. \tag{14.14}$$

Let:

$$\bar{x} = \sum_{i=1}^{10\,000} x_i/10\,000 \tag{14.15}$$

then:

$$\bar{x} \sim \mathsf{N}\left[\mu, 1/TM\right] = \mathsf{N}\left[6, 1/500\,000\right]. \tag{14.16}$$

The sample variance $\mathcal{V}[\bar{x}]$ will decrease as the Monte Carlo replication sample size M increases. In this instance, we can check that anticipated outcome against the sample result to analyze $\bar{x}$ as an estimator of μ, using PcNaive. The experiment of $M = 10\,000$ trials at $\mu = 6$ and $T = 50$ yields:

$$\bar{x} = 5.9995\ (0.0014) \tag{14.17}$$

where the number in parentheses is the estimate from the Monte Carlo of the standard error of $\bar{x}$ (namely $\tilde{\sigma}/\sqrt{M} \simeq 1/\sqrt{TM}$) called the Monte Carlo standard error (MCSE). The feasible range for $\mathcal{E}[\bar{x}] = \mu$ is small given the value of the estimated standard error, so the Monte Carlo is quite precise. Indeed, from (14.4), an approximate 95% confidence interval for μ is given by $[5.9967 \rightarrow 6.0023]$.

We could proceed to repeat this entire experiment at many different points in the parameter space, but instead will progress in a different way by developing more efficient Monte Carlo procedures which will achieve the same goal but both more accurately and more generally.

14.3 Sophisticated Monte Carlo

Despite the precision of the outcome in §14.2, it is useful to highlight the distinction between distribution sampling and genuine Monte Carlo. The above approach actually is naive, and at best has an accuracy which improves at a rate of $1/\sqrt{M}$ for a given T. This generates rapid improvements for little cost initially (e.g., consider an increase in M from 25 to 100 replications: accuracy doubles on average), and is a sound basis for pilot, or illustrative, Monte Carlo based solely on distribution sampling. However, high accuracy is hard to achieve, especially for (say) test powers where the probability of a rejection is p, and the usual average of the binary estimator (unity if reject, zero otherwise) has a standard error of $s = \sqrt{(\mathsf{p}[1-\mathsf{p}]/M)}$. For example, if $\mathsf{p} = 0.05$, then $s = 0.0022$ even when $M = 10\,000$, so that a 95% confidence interval around the estimated p is about 17% of p. Thus, there is a clear interest in deriving more efficient methods despite the relatively low cost of computer time.

14.3.1 Antithetic variates

The first efficient Monte Carlo method we consider is known as the method of antithetic variates. Record the first $x_1(\epsilon_1 \ldots \epsilon_{50})$. Since the $\{\epsilon_t\}$ are random, so are the $\{-\epsilon_t\}$, and from (14.12), exploiting the symmetry of the distribution only, each $-\epsilon_t$ is as likely to occur as the corresponding ϵ_t. Thus, calculate:

$$x_1^+ \left(-\epsilon_1 \ldots -\epsilon_{50}\right)$$

which in turn is as likely to occur as the original $x_1(\epsilon_1 \ldots \epsilon_{50})$. Since each of x_1 and x_1^+ is an unbiased estimator of μ, so is their average $\widetilde{x}$:

$$\widetilde{x} = \tfrac{1}{2}\left(x_1 + x_1^+\right), \tag{14.18}$$

with:

$$\mathcal{E}[\widetilde{x}] = \mu.$$

However, since:

$$x_1 = \mu + \sum_{t=1}^{T} \epsilon_t/50 \text{ and } x_1^+ = \mu - \sum_{t=1}^{T} \epsilon_t/50,$$

then, in fact:

$$\widetilde{x} \equiv \mu.$$

But this must occur in every trial of matched pairs, so:

$$\mathcal{V}[\widetilde{x}] \equiv 0.$$

Thus, we have proved in *two* replications that the sample mean is an unbiased estimator of the population mean for all possible values of μ: this is a distinct saving over naive simulation.

Antithetic variates can be used to establish the unbiasedness of some estimators which are too complex to analyze algebraically, and are members of a class of sophisticated Monte Carlo methods called variance reduction techniques (see e.g. Hammersley and Handscomb, 1964, Hendry and Trivedi, 1972, and Hendry, 1984). Unfortunately, antithetic variates of the variety $\{\epsilon_t\}$ followed by $\{-\epsilon_t\}$, as used above, do not always work well, even for symmetric distributions.

Example AR(1) process

Consider an example where the DGP is a zero-mean, first-order autoregressive process:

$$y_t = \alpha y_{t-1} + \epsilon_t \text{ with } \epsilon_t \sim \text{IN}\left[0, \sigma^2\right], \tag{14.19}$$

where $|\alpha| < 1$ and $y_0 = 0$. Now, switching the sign of $\{\epsilon_t\}$ switches the sign of $\{y_t\}$. Since the ordinary least squares (OLS) estimator of α in the econometric model is:

$$\widehat{\alpha} = \sum_{t=1}^{T} y_t y_{t-1} / \sum_{t=1}^{T} y_{t-1}^2 = \alpha + \sum_{t=1}^{T} y_{t-1}\epsilon_t / \sum_{t=1}^{T} y_{t-1}^2 = x_1 \text{ (here)}, \tag{14.20}$$

then the sign of $\widehat{\alpha}$ is unaffected by changing the sign of all the $\{\epsilon_t\}$ and hence:

$$x_1(\epsilon_1 \ldots \epsilon_T) \equiv x_1^+(-\epsilon_1 \ldots -\epsilon_T). \tag{14.21}$$

Thus, the repeated trial is simply wasted, and an efficiency loss results.

14.3.2 Control variables

An alternative approach to variance reduction is provided by the method of control variables. The reason for using Monte Carlo to study the distribution of (say) $\widehat{\alpha}$ in (14.20) is the mathematical intractability of deriving exact sampling results, due to the dependence between the numerator and denominator in (14.20). That does not entail that all aspects of the problem are intractable.

Example AR(1) process *(continued)*

First, we can calculate the moments of the $\{y_t\}$ in (14.19):

$$E[y_t] = 0,$$

$$E[y_t^2] \simeq \frac{\sigma^2}{1 - \alpha^2},$$

and:

$$E[y_t y_{t-1}] \simeq \frac{\alpha \sigma^2}{1 - \alpha^2}.$$

The use of the approximation sign is due to having assumed that $y_0 = 0$. Consequently, we can derive:

$$E\left[T^{-1} \sum_{t=1}^{T} y_t y_{t-1}\right] \simeq \frac{\alpha \sigma^2}{1 - \alpha^2},$$

and:

$$E\left[T^{-1} \sum_{t=1}^{T} y_{t-1}^2\right] \simeq \frac{\sigma^2}{1 - \alpha^2}.$$

Although we know the expectations of the numerator and denominator of $\widehat{\alpha}$ separately, their dependence entails that:

$$E[\widehat{\alpha}] \neq \frac{E\left[\sum_{t=1}^{T} y_t y_{t-1}\right]}{E\left[\sum_{t=1}^{T} y_{t-1}^2\right]}.$$

Second, the distribution of $\widehat{\alpha}$ in large samples is known to be:

$$\sqrt{T}\left(\widehat{\alpha} - \alpha\right) \xrightarrow{D} N\left[0, \left(1 - \alpha^2\right)\right]. \tag{14.22}$$

Third, let us invent a new 'estimator' $\widetilde{\alpha}$, which will be our control variable, defined by:

$$\widetilde{\alpha} = \alpha + T^{-1} \sum_{t=1}^{T} y_{t-1} \epsilon_t / \left[\sigma^2 / \left(1 - \alpha^2\right)\right]. \tag{14.23}$$

We can calculate $\widetilde{\alpha}$ in a Monte Carlo, since we know, or generate, all of its components, even though we could not calculate it in any practical econometric analysis where (α, σ) and $\{\epsilon_t\}$ are unknown. The construction of $\widetilde{\alpha}$ is based on $\widehat{\alpha}$, but replaces the denominator of the latter by its population value, scaled to the relevant sample size T. Three important consequences follow. First, from (14.23):

$$\mathcal{E}\left[\widetilde{\alpha}\right] = \alpha + \mathcal{E}\left[T^{-1}\sum_{t=1}^{T} y_{t-1}\epsilon_t\right] / \left[\sigma^2 / \left(1 - \alpha^2\right)\right] = \alpha.$$

Thus, in the Monte Carlo, $\widetilde{\alpha}$ is an unbiased estimator of α. With some algebra it can be shown that:

$$\mathcal{V}\left[\widetilde{\alpha}\right] = \left(1 - \alpha^2\right)/T.$$

Hence, from Cramér's theorem, $\sqrt{T}(\widetilde{\alpha} - \alpha)$ has the same limiting distribution as $\sqrt{T}(\widehat{\alpha} - \alpha)$ (see Hendry, 1995b):

$$\sqrt{T}\left(\widetilde{\alpha} - \alpha\right) \xrightarrow{D} \mathsf{N}\left[0, \left(1 - \alpha^2\right)\right]. \tag{14.24}$$

Consequently:

$$\sqrt{T}\left(\widehat{\alpha} - \widetilde{\alpha}\right) \xrightarrow{P} 0.$$

In fact, for the present problem (and usually true in stationary processes), $(\widehat{\alpha} - \widetilde{\alpha})$ is $O_p(T^{-1})$ (of order in probability of T^{-1}: see Mann and Wald, 1943), and so that is the approximate rate at which their difference vanishes. This contrasts with the original formulation in terms of $(\widehat{\alpha} - \alpha)$ which is $O_p(T^{-1/2})$. Finally, in the identity:

$$\widehat{\alpha} \equiv \widetilde{\alpha} + (\widehat{\alpha} - \widetilde{\alpha}), \tag{14.25}$$

the first term on the right has a known expectation, and the second is $O_p(1/T)$. Thus, a more precise outcome can be obtained by calculating $\widehat{\alpha}$ and $\widetilde{\alpha}$ in every replication, recording their difference and at the completion of the replications adding back the known value of $\mathcal{E}[\widetilde{\alpha}]$, which corresponds to using the Monte Carlo estimator $\breve{\alpha}$:

$$\breve{\alpha} = \widehat{\alpha} - \widetilde{\alpha} + \mathcal{E}\left[\widetilde{\alpha}\right] \text{ where } \mathcal{E}\left[\breve{\alpha}\right] \equiv \mathcal{E}\left[\widehat{\alpha}\right]. \tag{14.26}$$

An alternative interpretation of the role of control variables is to note that (14.23) defines a function of the $\{\epsilon_t\}$ which can help control for variation in the Monte Carlo due to the particular random numbers generated. That notion is similar to the role of antithetic variates above, and continuing that reasoning, we see that:

$$\mathcal{V}\left[\breve{\alpha}\right] = \mathcal{V}\left[\widehat{\alpha} - \widetilde{\alpha}\right] = \mathcal{V}\left[\widehat{\alpha}\right] + \mathcal{V}\left[\widetilde{\alpha}\right] - 2\mathcal{C}\left[\widehat{\alpha}, \widetilde{\alpha}\right] \leq \mathcal{V}\left[\widehat{\alpha}\right], \tag{14.27}$$

if:

$$\mathcal{V}\left[\widetilde{\alpha}\right] \leq 2\mathcal{C}\left[\widehat{\alpha}, \widetilde{\alpha}\right].$$

The variance of the controlled experiment will be less than that of the uncontrolled if the correlation between $\widehat{\alpha}$ and $\widetilde{\alpha}$ is sufficiently high, which it must be for large enough T from Cramér's theorem (see e.g., Sargan, 1988). Since the costs of experiments rise with T, an increasing efficiency gain provides the perfect foil by allowing a commensurate reduction in the number of trials needed to attain a given accuracy (see Hendry, 1974).

There is a close link between control variates and asymptotic distribution theory in the above approach. In effect, the control variable simulates the limiting distribution directly in finite samples. Other functions of the $\{\epsilon_t\}$ than those based on Cramér's theorem could be used to control the experimental variation, but may not yield large improvements in precision. Ripley (1987) and Davidson and MacKinnon (1990) consider the use of control variables whose effects can be estimated by inter-replication regression (rather than having a known coefficient of unity as in (14.25) above).

14.3.3 Common random numbers

At first sight, this so-called sophisticated method seems both rudimentary and potentially invalid. The basic theorem explicitly required independent sampling, and reusing random numbers clearly violates that assumption. However, we have already seen that antithetic variates reused the random numbers to good effect after a sign change, and control variables used more complicated functions of them, so we consider reusing the random numbers without any alteration.

Early studies (such as Summers, 1965) automatically reused random numbers for studying inter-estimator behaviour, simply by the natural practice of applying all the methods under study to the same data set at each replication. The difference between two unbiased estimators remains an unbiased estimator of the difference, even if the estimators are dependent, but the variance of the estimated difference will be smaller if there is positive dependence. If sampling variation leads to over (under)-estimation in the first estimate, the dependence leads to a similar over (under)-estimation in the second estimate, so this contamination is reduced by examining their difference. Thus, positive dependence can be beneficial. We will see the dramatic gains possible from this method in relation to establishing invariance in §14.4, and also lesser but still useful gains in recursive methods in §14.6.

Figure 14.2b and c illustrate the impact of common random numbers in recursive Monte Carlo. In the first, common random numbers are used, so that (e.g.) the first replication at $T = 40$ and at $T = 50$ have the same 40 data values in common. In Figure 14.2c there is no overlap in the data.

14.4 Invariance

Next, we will investigate the extent to which specificity can be reduced by invariance arguments, which would also help offset the expense in time and energy of undertaking many experiments. Reconsider the simulation of the sample mean (14.11), and rewrite (14.12) as:

$$y_t - \mu = \epsilon_t.$$

Surprisingly, therefore, we need only analyze the $\{\epsilon_t\}$ in the experiments, calculate $\bar{\epsilon}$, $V[\bar{\epsilon}]$ etc., and at the end recover the relevant function of $\bar{y}$ from:

$$\bar{y} \equiv \mu + \bar{\epsilon}.$$

What is true for $\bar{\epsilon}$, however, holds for all $(\bar{y} - \mu)$. Hence, the results are not specific to $\mu = 6$.

Repeating this experiment for the same μ and a different seed would produce another sample of $\{y_i\}$ from the population of all possible experiments. However, repeating the experiment for a different μ, but the same seed for the random numbers, would generate identical outcomes as we have just shown. Thus, this application of common random numbers (see §14.3.3) has infinite efficiency relative to independent sampling as μ changes. Similar arguments should convince you that σ^2 is also irrelevant to the behavior of $\bar{y}$ as an estimator of μ, beyond being a scaling factor. The transform:

$$(y_t - \mu)/\sigma \sim \mathsf{IN}[0, 1]$$

defines a canonical experiment in this context from which the outcomes for all other values of μ and $\sigma > 0$ can be obtained by multiplication (for σ) or addition (for μ). In more complicated DGPs, invariance arguments can still be used for many estimators of interest (see Breusch and Pagan, 1980). For example, in (14.19), $\widehat{\alpha}$ is also independent of σ, as can be demonstrated numerically by using the same random numbers at two values of σ, and showing that $\widehat{\alpha}$ is unaltered.

Example AR(1) process *(continued)*

Figure 14.1 shows the histogram of the $\{x_i, \ i = 1, \dots, M\}$ from estimating (14.19) with $\alpha = 0.8$ for $T = 20$ using $M = 10\,000$, together with a (non-parametrically estimated) density function. Both graphs are approximating the unknown distribution:

$$\mathsf{D}_x\left(x \mid \mu, \ \sigma^2\right) \quad \text{where } \mu = \mathsf{E}\left[\widehat{\alpha}\right] \text{ and } \sigma^2 = \mathsf{V}\left[\widehat{\alpha}\right]. \tag{14.28}$$

The shape of the estimated density is highly skewed and non-normal. However, neither the scale nor the shape depends on σ^2 (although both depend on α and T).

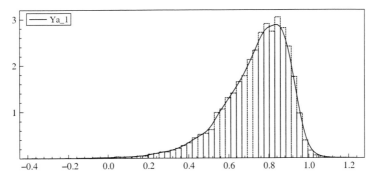

Figure 14.1 Histogram and density from AR(1) process.

14.5 Asymptotic analysis

It may seem odd to assign a specific role to asymptotic analysis in Monte Carlo, given that the main reason for adopting simulation is to investigate finite-sample behaviour. However, asymptotic analysis can play a very important role, not least by helping to evaluate when large-sample approximations are likely to be good or not. Indeed, it is perhaps more fruitful to pose the question 'How small is small?' rather than the converse 'How large is large?' in designing simulation studies. An example of the power of asymptotic theory to elucidate a complicated Monte Carlo study is provided in Hendry (1973).

We distinguish four roles for asymptotics in simulation based finite-sample studies of stationary stochastic processes: §14.5.1 designing experiments; §14.5.2 evaluating the role of sample size; §14.5.3 controlling inter-experiment variability; §14.5.4 elucidating test power behaviour. These are considered in turn. Chapter 16 considers the details of asymptotic analysis when applied to a small dynamic system, based on Hendry (1979a, 1982).

14.5.1 The design of Monte Carlo experiments

Section 14.7 focuses on experimental design in general, and here we only consider the issue of how to choose the points in the parameter space that merit study. Since both the finite sample and the asymptotic properties of estimators and other statistics depend on the underlying DGP, it is important to conduct a 'representative' set of experiments. Good prior guidance on problematic or well-behaved regions of the parameter space can be obtained at little cost by numerically evaluating the asymptotic behaviour of the relevant statistics. For example, in the first-order stationary autoregression in (14.19), the limiting distribution is given in (14.22). This suggests that points near the unit circle may be problematic as the variance tends to zero. It is trivial to evaluate the probability limit of the estimator and its estimated standard error in such a case, but the approach applies more generally. Chapter 16 discusses its implementation in a small, linear stationary system. Ericsson (1991) provides a detailed discussion.

14.5.2 How small is small?

Is a Monte Carlo study needed at all? Clearly, to begin to answer this question, some analytical or simulation study is required. However, as we saw in §14.3.2, approximations to estimators can be derived from control variables which are distributed in the simulation as the small-sample analogue of the limiting distribution. Thus, a minimal requirement of any detailed simulation study is that it be at least as accurate as the control variable (i.e., $O_p(T^{-1})$). In effect, the simulation is conceived of as studying deviations from the limiting distribution as a baseline, rather than from zero. As will be seen in several instances below, assuming stationarity (except near the unit circle, when a different limiting distribution theory based on 'near-integrated' processes applies, as in Phillips, 1988), asymptotic behaviour can account for much of the observed inter-experiment variation in simulation studies.

14.5.3 Controlling inter-experiment variability

The last comment of the previous sub-section suggests the road ahead: calculate the asymptotic outcome for the numerical value of the parameter vector which defines the experiment, and use that known value to help control for variations in outcomes between different points in the parameter space. Thus, we conceptually imagine three reasons for changes in (say) an estimated bias between two points in $\Psi \times \mathcal{T}$, namely, sampling variation (due to using different random numbers), changes in the asymptotic outcomes as ψ alters (which we can calculate numerically), and changes in the deviation of the actual finite-sample outcomes from their asymptotic counterparts (which are the real focus of the Monte Carlo and depend on the sample sizes considered).

As §14.8 will elucidate, we can exploit knowledge of the asymptotic results by using them as an argument in a response surface characterizing the simulation results as a function of the asymptotic results. Again taking (14.22) as an example, for different values of α, the Monte Carlo sampling standard deviation (MCSD) of OLS will alter. Such changes are due in part to Monte Carlo sampling fluctuations, to changes in the sample size, and to changes in α. If both the MCSD and the limiting standard deviation are standardized for sample size, then most of the observed variability in the former is usually due to changes in the latter (see e.g., Hendry, 1979a). Denote the MCSD in the kth of K experiments at different points in $\Psi \times \mathcal{T}$ by MCSD_k. Then, one could base a response surface for MCSD on:

$$\mathrm{MCSD}_k = f\left(\left[\sqrt{1 - \alpha^2/T_k}\right], \alpha_k, T_k\right) \qquad (14.29)$$

for $k = 1, \ldots, K$, where we anticipate a unit effect from the first (asymptotic) term, and the remaining terms in $f([\cdot], \alpha_k, T_k)$ represent finite-sample effects. A log transform of both sides would ensure positive predictions for MCSD from (14.29), and a common functional form for variances and standard deviations. Similar considerations apply when the estimated coefficient or equation standard error is inconsistent for the MCSD: see §15.7 for further details.

14.5.4 Elucidating test powers

This is really a continuation of the idea embodied in (14.29), but applied to test powers, where the empirical rejection frequency is estimated by $\tilde{p}$ and the asymptotic local power is p^* (see Ch. 16 for more details). A logit equation seems a sensible choice to link $\tilde{p}$ and p^*, as it ensures predictions in $[0, 1]$ and is easy to estimate. In such equations, p^* often accounts for the bulk of the observed variance across experiments in $\tilde{p}$ (see e.g. Mizon and Hendry, 1980, and Cox, 1970). The logit form can be specified for both sizes and powers, as well as be formulated to embody any known small-sample approximations to test powers (see §15.7.4 and, e.g., Hendry, 1984, Ericsson, 1986, and Hendry and Neale, 1991).

14.6 Recursive Monte Carlo

14.6.1 Introduction: estimating the sample mean

The second important specificity of the experiments so far is analyzing only one sample size T. This limitation can be overcome by a different approach, known as recursive Monte Carlo (see Hendry and Neale, 1987). Instead of simply calculating the Monte Carlo at the largest sample size T, it is possible to compute all the relevant statistics recursively as the sample is generated, from T_0 (the smallest feasible sample size of interest) up to T. We begin by considering the formulae for estimating the sample mean, as a straightforward special case of the result for least squares estimation. The approach in PcNaive, however, is more general, allowing any choice of sample sizes, $T_0, T_1, \ldots, T$.

Let $\overline{y}_\tau$ be the mean for a sample of size τ then, for $\tau = T_0, \ldots, T$:

$$\overline{y}_\tau = \frac{1}{\tau} \sum_{t=1}^{\tau} y_t = \frac{1}{\tau} y_\tau + \frac{\tau - 1}{\tau} \overline{y}_{\tau-1} = w_\tau y_\tau + (1 - w_\tau) \overline{y}_{\tau-1}. \tag{14.30}$$

Once $\overline{y}_{j-1}$ is known for any j, the next $\overline{y}_j$ is trivial to calculate as a weighted average of the new y_j and the previous mean. Consequently, the $\overline{y}$ at each τ is updated in a similar way at every replication. Here is an apparently 'free lunch', namely $(T - T_0)$ values of $\{\overline{y}_t\}$, rather than just the full sample mean, for little extra computational cost. Similar recursive formulae can be obtained for calculating variances and so on. However, the labour costs of implementing the recursive formulae tend to preclude their use, as does the feature to allow more general sequences of sample sizes (although the 'gaps' can more than make up for the benefit of the recursive updating formulae).

Note that the output is massive: $(T - T_0 + 1) \times M$ values for each statistic invest-igated! Fortunately, we can analyze the behaviour of statistics across sample sizes by graphical methods, e.g., by reporting the mean across replications and plus or minus twice its Monte Carlo standard error at each sample size.

Example $\mathsf{IN}[\mu, \sigma^2]$ process *(continued)*

Figure 14.2b shows the values of $\{\widetilde{x}_j - \mu\}$ at each $j \in [T_0, T]$ for the §14.2 example of estimating a sample mean, using $T_0 = 10$, $T = 50$, $M = 10\,000$. The bias is close to zero in absolute terms, and the expected value of $\overline{y}_t$ has a small confidence interval at every sample size. It can be verified that the MCSE does indeed decline at the rate of $(TM)^{-1/2}$. From a weak law of large numbers:

$$\overline{y}_T \xrightarrow{P} \mu \text{ as } T \to \infty, \tag{14.31}$$

and since $\widetilde{x}_T = \sum x_{i,T}/M$, where each $x_{i,T}$ is a value of $\overline{y}_T$:

$$\widetilde{x}_T \xrightarrow{P} \mu \text{ as } T \to \infty. \tag{14.32}$$

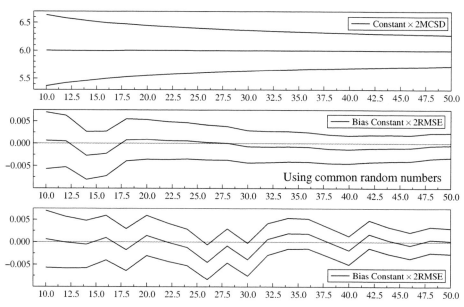

Figure 14.2   Recursive mean and bias from $\mathsf{IN}[\mu, \sigma^2]$ process.

Thus, the uncertainty in estimating the unknown mean decreases as τ increases, at the rate $\tau^{-1/2}$. All of the confidence intervals for $(\mathcal{E}[\widetilde{x}] - \mu)$ include zero and range from $(-0.007, 0.007)$ at $T_0 = 10$ to $(-0.0033, 0.0023)$ at $T = 50$, a reduction of about 50% as anticipated from statistical theory.

Despite the small size of the uncertainty measures, $\{\widetilde{x}_j\}$ wanders rather erratically as j changes, especially given that the figure reports the average across $10\,000$ independent samples. The explanation for that phenomenon follows from an analysis of martingales. Let:

$$S_\tau = \sum_{t=1}^{\tau} (y_t - \mu) \tag{14.33}$$

then:

$$S_\tau = S_{\tau-1} + (y_t - \mu) \tag{14.34}$$

and hence:

$$\mathsf{E}\left[S_\tau \mid S_{\tau-1}\right] = S_{\tau-1}. \tag{14.35}$$

Consequently:

$$(y_t - \mu) = \tau^{-1} S_\tau \tag{14.36}$$

which is a 'scaled' martingale (but is heteroscedastic), so its behaviour derives from that of the martingale, as does that of $\widetilde{x}$. Since martingales act like random walks, it is unsurprising that a single realization can manifest 'wandering' behaviour.

14.6.2 The general approach

The previous sections deliberately isolated T from the rest of the parameter space $\boldsymbol{\Psi}$, given the fundamental role which T (or perhaps $\sqrt{T}$) plays in Monte Carlo work on finite-sample distributions. Frequently, it would be desirable to formulate response surfaces based on many different values T_i for each selected point $\psi_i \in \boldsymbol{\Psi}$. In recursive Monte Carlo, this typically requires a separate experiment for each combination of T_i and ψ_i, which can be quite expensive (e.g. $T_i = 25, 50, 100, 200$ etc.). The cost can be kept down by a judicious choice of sample sizes. By using common random numbers, we obtain a proper recursive MC: the first 25 observations for $T_i = 50$ (say), are precisely the observations used for $T_i = 25$.

In a recursive framework, successive results are not independent and so are not equivalent to conducting separate experiments: whilst the random numbers used remain random, they are not independent over T_i for a given ψ_i (see the discussion of common random numbers in Hendry, 1984), although they will be independent for given T_i, or over T_i, between ψ_i and ψ_k, assuming different seeds are used in different experiments.

In the present context, recursion also acts as a variance reduction technique. By using the same stream of random numbers as T_i varies, the estimate of the outcome difference between T_j and T_i $(j > i)$ will have lower variance than if separate independent streams of random numbers were used. This corresponds to the conventional practice, when studying two or more estimators, of using the same data to analyze all the different estimators in order to increase the precision of inter-estimator comparisons as in §14.3 above.

Gains from recursive Monte Carlo procedures potentially apply to all results from models obtainable from the DGP, including most types of mis-specifications, as well as the properties of test statistics used to detect such mis-specifications. Also, with the recursive procedures, 'post-estimation-sample forecast tests' become relatively redundant, since forecast test statistics can be computed recursively for any length of forecast within the sample T.

Issues of estimator behaviour as sample size alters could have been studied in a conventional Monte Carlo, but there are also problems which conventional techniques handle poorly, involving much greater cost or considerably more specificity and uncertainty. One obvious example is the performance of estimators and tests when a structural break occurs in the DGP. In its broadest interpretation, a structural break means introducing parameter variation into the DGP, from a simple blip effect in a coefficient of the DGP (at one point in the sample, a coefficient changes value then immediately reverts to its former value), through similar step and trend changes in coefficients, to parameter variation schemes of the random walk variety, as well as non-linear parameter changes over time. The study of parameter variation was the *sine qua non* of early work with recursive least squares estimators (Teräsvirta, 1970, and Brown, Durbin and Evans, 1975), so it is natural to extend such an approach to recursive Monte Carlo (see Hendry and Neale, 1987, 1991).

From the teaching perspective, with graphical computer facilities, recursive procedures offer excellent classroom demonstrations of absolute and comparative properties of estimators and tests, under correct and incorrect specifications, as the sample size varies from very small to fairly large (including possibly the asymptotic outcomes).

14.6.3 Recursive updating of Monte Carlo calculations

Recursion can also be implemented to good effect across replications even in conventional Monte Carlo analyses of econometric estimators and test statistics, when the main interest is in the first two moments of the simulation results. These can be obtained by using updating formulae for the simulation mean and standard deviation (analogously for other moments):

$$\mu_{i+1} = (i+1)^{-1} \left[i\mu_i + \zeta_{i+1} \right],$$

for the mean μ of a variable ζ; and for the standard deviation:

$$\sigma_{i+1}^2 = ([i-1]/i)\sigma_i^2 + (i+1)^{-1}[\zeta_{i+1} - \mu_i]^2.$$

The advantages of such 'on-line' updating are both an inexpensive update and allowing calculations to be interrupted at any stage yet be accurate and complete at that point. The cost is a slight loss in numerical accuracy, which in this case will not normally be noticeable.

In earlier chapters, we used Monte Carlo in both its modes: across replications at a given t to study bias; and across t for all replications to consider convergence issues.

14.7 Experimental design

There is too vast a literature on experimental design for us to hope to provide even a summary in a book of this nature, and we merely note a few possibilities: good general references are Cochran and Cox (1957) and Cox (1958). First, the design must cover the parameter space adequately, unless only a pilot study is envisaged. Secondly, for a given budget cost, there is a trade-off between fewer but more precise experiments and more but less precise ones: as yet little seems to be known about the optimal choice, but neither extreme seems desirable (i.e. a single experiment with a huge number of replications precluding response surfaces, or one replication per experiment where MCSD could not be calculated). Next, orthogonal designs seem preferable to collinear ones so the separate effects of design parameters are easily distinguished. Often, a confounded design is adopted where only a subset of a complete set of orthogonal experiments is conducted. A simplistic example is selecting the first and the fourth elements of $\alpha \in \{-0.5, 0.5\}$ and $T \in \{25, 100\}$ so that the pairs $[-0.5, 25]$ and $[0.5, 100]$ only are considered. Indeed, Hendry and Harrison (1974) chose design points randomly from a high dimensional orthogonal design space, testing their response surfaces on other random selected points, but confounding most higher-order interaction effects.

At a more sophisticated level, an iterative search design can be used to explore the parameter space for interesting regions (as an econometrics example, see Conlisk, 1974). Finally, the role of asymptotic distribution theory in selecting designs should not be neglected, as noted in §14.5.3 and §14.5.4 above.

14.8 Post-simulation analysis

Repeating experiments at many points in the design space raises the problem of summarizing the mass of results generated. Tabulation is possible, but is both hard to remember and not conducive to general findings — graphical presentation of the results is usually much more incisive. The need to summarize, and the aim of simulation itself, both motivate a more general technique known as response surfaces. Chapter 15 discusses response surfaces in detail, here we motivate the approach.

The usual objective in a Monte Carlo study is not simply to calculate the properties of a distribution at a few points in the parameter space, but to solve the analogue of the corresponding mathematical analysis, which would be applicable to the complete parameter space. The DGP is the joint density of the observables given the parameters, and for different parameter values, different samples of observables result. In turn, the distributions of statistics of interest depend on the parameters of the DGP. For example,

$E[\widehat{\alpha}]$, the expected value of the OLS estimator from (14.20), depends on α and T, and can be written as the conditional expectation:

$$E\left[\widehat{\alpha} \mid \alpha, T\right] = G(\alpha, T). \tag{14.37}$$

In principle, σ also might matter, but it does not do so here. Thus, we re-state the objective of Monte Carlo studies of finite-sample behaviour of statistics as numerically establishing functions like $G(\alpha, T)$.

We know the large-sample behaviour of the OLS estimator of α from (14.22), so the limiting form of the function $G(\cdot)$ can be deduced, and this can aid formulating the response surface approximating $G(\alpha, T)$. Specifically, since $\widehat{\alpha}$ is consistent for α and has a symmetric asymptotic distribution, a first approximation to the unknown function $G(\alpha, T)$ in (14.37) might take the form $H(\alpha, T)$, where:

$$
\begin{aligned}
H(\alpha, T) &= \alpha + \gamma_1 \frac{\alpha}{T} + \gamma_2 \frac{\alpha}{T^2} + \cdots \\
&\approx G(\alpha, T).
\end{aligned}
\tag{14.38}
$$

The form of $H(\alpha, T)$ ensures consistency because $H(\alpha, T) \rightarrow \alpha$ as $T \rightarrow \infty$ and asymptotic unbiasedness because $T^{1/2}[H(\alpha, T) - \alpha] \rightarrow 0$ as $T \rightarrow \infty$. Given simulation results from a set of experiments across a range of values of α and T, the unknown γ_i could be estimated by regression of the (observed) Monte Carlo estimates of $E[\widehat{\alpha}]$ on α, α/T, α/T^2, etc. Response surfaces for higher-order moments, test powers, etc., can be developed in a similar fashion, and are described below. Cochran and Cox (1957, p.335ff, p.369) and Cox (1958, p.113–128), discuss the use of response surfaces in statistical analyses. Their use in econometrics is relatively recent (and not particularly widespread) although they were proposed at least as early as Summers, 1959; see Summers, 1965 and Sowey, 1973.

14.9 Random number generation

The basic random numbers generated for experiments using PcNaive are uniformly distributed values in the unit interval [denoted $u_i \sim U(0, 1)$], from a user-selected 'seed' u_0 so that experiments can be replicated. Since random numbers are at the heart of any distribution sampling procedure, they must appropriately mimic the desired stochastic processes, although this requirement does not imply that the random numbers must be generated by an analogue of the random process (physical devices have sometimes been used — see Tocher, 1963, however, these tend to be a poor source of random numbers).

The basic random numbers u_i in most computer experiments are produced by deterministic algorithms such as e.g. the congruential generator (see Ripley, 1987):

$$z_{i+1} = (bz_i + c) \bmod r \quad \text{for } i = 0, 1, \ldots, m, \tag{14.39}$$

with

$$u_i = z_i/r \in [0, 1].$$

Good choices of b, c and r are important for avoiding autocorrelation, maintaining uniformity and producing the maximum feasible period m. If any study depends on some particular feature of the $\{u_i\}$, then it is essential to test this feature given the random numbers actually used in the experiment (see e.g. Park and Miller, 1988). The $\{u_i\}$ are really only pseudo-random, in that from knowing the algorithm and the 'seed' z_0, they can be exactly reproduced. Nevertheless, they should not be detectably non-random on statistical tests. There is a large literature on random number generation, which we cannot even summarize (useful discussions are provided by Devroye, 1986, Dagpunar, 1988, Hammersley and Handscomb, 1964, Gentle, 1998, Kennedy and Gentle, 1980, Klein, 1974, Naylor, 1971, Ripley, 1987, and Tocher, 1963). The methods used in Ox are based on more advanced approaches; for more detail consult Doornik (2001).

Other distributions can be derived from the uniform distribution using the property:

$$\Pr(u_i \le k) = \mathsf{P}(k) = k \text{ for } u_i \sim \mathsf{U}(0, 1) \text{ and } k \in [0, 1]. \tag{14.40}$$

Consequently, $\mathsf{P}(k)$ and k can be interchanged in any derivation. Let $F(\cdot)$ denote the cumulative distribution function of a random variable $\{e_i\}$; if $F(\cdot)$ can be analytically inverted, then $e_i = F^{-1}(u_i)$ implies that $u_i = F(e_i)$ and hence:

$$\Pr(e_i \le k) = \Pr(F(e_i) \le F(k)) = \Pr(u_i \le F(k)) = \mathsf{P}(F(k)) = F(k). \tag{14.41}$$

as required. Using the exponential distribution as an example, $F(\cdot) = 1 - \exp(-\mu\epsilon)$ where $\mu > 0$:

$$\epsilon_i = -\mu^{-1}\log(1 - u_i) \sim F(\cdot). \tag{14.42}$$

Unfortunately, the normal distribution does not have an analytical inverse and two possible methods (other, faster methods are available) for generating $e_i \sim \mathsf{IN}[0, 1]$ are the approximate central limit result:

$$\left(\sum_{j=1}^{12} u_j - 6\right) = e_i, \tag{14.43}$$

and for the bivariate normal, the Box–Müller method:

$$(e_i, e_{i+1}) = h_i(\cos 2\pi u_{i+1}, \sin 2\pi u_{i+1}) \text{ where } h_i = (-2\log u_i)^{\frac{1}{2}}. \tag{14.44}$$

A well-tested and empirically-satisfactory generator must be used for input to the Box–Müller method when (u_i, u_{i+1}) are successively generated. Ox uses the polar-Marsaglia method (Marsaglia and Bray, 1964), which avoids the trigonometric functions. From the basic random numbers, random variates with a wide range of distributional shapes can be constructed. The Ox book lists those available in Ox, and briefly describes their methods of generation.

To mimic the stationary state of a dynamic ergodic process, random numbers can be discarded at each replication prior to constructing artificial data variables. Alternatively, the equilibrium means can be used, perhaps based on a prior asymptotic analysis (see Ch. 16). In processes with a unit root, the initialization must be done carefully, as the effect of the initial value persists. Often, the theory derivation assumes $y_0 = 0$, so that should be set in the simulation. Finally, PcNaive also allows data initial values to be input.

Chapter 15

Response surfaces

15.1 Introduction

Returning now to a pure distribution sampling approach, we discuss how to overcome the limitation that the results of any single experiment are specific to the parameter value and sample size used. For example, the Monte Carlo study in §14.4 is specific to the one value of $\mu = 6$, the implicit value of $\sigma^2 = 1$, and the single sample size $T = 50$. This chapter investigates how to resolve that difficulty by repeating experiments for a range of relevant values of the DGP's parameters and the econometric sample size T. The next section introduces the general problem that is addressed by response surfaces, motivating their use by considering the problem of estimating the bias of OLS for the AR(1) model. Thereafter, we derive heteroscedasticity corrections for response surfaces, construct ways of evaluating their validity, and formulate specific response surfaces for first and second moments, estimated standard errors, and test rejection frequencies.

15.2 The general approach

Monte Carlo begins with the choice of objective and the design of the experiments to be conducted. The objective is understanding the finite-sample properties of some estimator or test statistic (denoted τ), which is obtained from estimating the econometric relationship (or relationships) of interest. This relationship of interest may differ from the data generation process (DGP), which specifies how the data appearing in the relationship of interest are actually generated. The DGP is defined by its parameters, which are now also Monte Carlo design variables (denoted ψ), and by the econometric sample size T. In the notation from above, the ranges of ψ and T are given by the parameter space Ψ and the sample-size space $\mathcal{T}$:

$$\psi \in \Psi \text{ and } T \in \mathcal{T} = [T_a, T_b],$$

where T_a and T_b are the smallest and largest econometric sample sizes considered. In short, the objective of the Monte Carlo study is to determine the finite-sample distribution of τ for a given DGP and relationship of interest over $\Psi \times T$.

More modestly, we focus on some property G_T of τ, where $G_T \equiv \mathsf{E}[\varphi(\tau)]$ and $\varphi(\cdot)$ is a function chosen by the investigator. In particular, $\varphi(\tau)$ might be a power of τ, or it could be an indicator function, in which case the expectation would become a rejection frequency. In any case, $\mathsf{E}[\varphi(\tau)]$ depends upon ψ and T and can be expressed as a conditional probability formula:

$$G_T \equiv \mathsf{E}\left[\varphi\left(\tau\right) \mid \psi, T\right] = G(\psi, T).$$

The exact functional form of $G(\psi, T)$ is often intractable, so a good approximation to it over $\Psi \times T$ is sought.

Thus, we re-state the objective of Monte Carlo studies of finite-sample behaviour of statistics as numerically establishing functions that accurately approximate $G(\psi, T)$. A single experiment determines one point on the conditional expectation function, and could be viewed as a 'pilot' study, whereas a set of experiments would enable the general conditional expectation $G(\psi, T)$ to be estimated (e.g. by regression) from the known (and given) parameter values and sample sizes. This approach would require the specification of how $G(\psi, T)$ depends on its arguments, and that can often be deduced in substantial measure from an asymptotic analysis of the relevant statistic (i.e., as $T \to \infty$).

When the large-sample behaviour of the estimator of interest can be derived, we can deduce the asymptotic properties of other relevant statistics in stationary processes, such as standard error estimators, t-tests etc, so the limiting forms of the function $G(\cdot, \cdot)$ usually can be derived for the statistic of interest. Designating the asymptotic part of $G(\psi, T)$ by $G_a(\psi, T)$, we have:

$$
\begin{aligned}
G\left(\psi, T\right) &= G_a\left(\psi, T\right) + \left[G\left(\psi, T\right) - G_a\left(\psi, T\right)\right] \\
&\equiv G_a\left(\psi, T\right) + G_f\left(\psi, T\right),
\end{aligned}
\tag{15.1}
$$

where we have decomposed the unknown function $G(\psi, T)$ into a known and analytically calculable part $G_a(\psi, T)$ and a purely finite-sample part $G_f(\psi, T)$ [$\equiv G(\psi, T) - G_a(\psi, T)$] which remains to be simulated.

This partitioning of $G(\psi, T)$ into known and unknown components helps reduce both imprecision and specificity. On the former, the term $G_f(\psi, T)$ is often of a smaller order in T than $G(\psi, T)$ is itself. Thus, what is being simulated is much smaller than it would have been otherwise. Specifically, by using asymptotic theory, we are able to simplify the problem of directly simulating $G(\psi, T)$ (usually of $O(1)$) to one of analytically calculating $G_a(\psi, T)$ and simulating only $G_f(\psi, T)$, which is $o(1)$ and often $O(T^{-1/2})$, or even $O(T^{-1})$. On the latter (specificity), the function $G_a(\psi, T)$ is completely general (i.e., valid for all ψ and T in $\Psi \times T$, although often it will not depend on T), and so the issue of specificity arises only insofar as the asymptotically negligible term $G_f(\psi, T)$ is approximated in the Monte Carlo. This approach is in line with the rubric in Hammersley and Handscomb (1964, pp.5,59) that one should solve as much of the problem as possible analytically in order to minimize the imprecision and specificity arising from simulation.

As noted in §14.5 above, the inter-experimental movements in $G(\psi, T)$ are often dominated by the asymptotic component $G_a(\psi, T)$, and not by the asymptotically-negligible component $G_f(\psi, T)$. In such cases, the asymptotic term $G_a(\psi, T)$ provides an informative summary and interpretation of the Monte Carlo simulations. Examples demonstrating the importance of asymptotics for interpreting Monte Carlo studies abound, including Hendry (1973) on inconsistent estimators, Nickell (1981) on the biases in dynamic models with fixed effects, and Ericsson (1986) on the powers of tests of nested and non-nested hypotheses. In each of these cases, the author shows how asymptotic theory captures the dominant movements in Monte Carlo evidence previously published by other authors.

Finally, $G_a(\psi, T)$ need not be the asymptotic component *per se*, but could be any analytically calculable formula, and in particular could include higher-order terms from some suitable expansion (e.g., an Edgeworth expansion). For example, in analyzing the Monte Carlo simulations of the mean-square error of dynamic forecasts in Orcutt and Winokur (1969), Ericsson and Marquez (1989) use formulae from Schmidt (1974) and Baillie (1979) which include terms through T^{-1}.

Example AR(1) process *(continued)*

To illustrate these concepts, consider a Monte Carlo for the AR(1) process. The data generation process is

$$y_t = \alpha y_{t-1} + \epsilon_t \text{ with } \epsilon_t \sim \text{IN}\left[0, \sigma^2\right], \ |\alpha| < 1, \ y_0 = 0,$$

the econometric relationship of interest coincides with the DGP in this case:

$$y_t = \alpha y_{t-1} + \epsilon_t.$$

The statistic investigated is the OLS estimator of α (denoted $\widehat{\alpha}$), and the parameter space is $\{|\alpha| < 1, \ T \in [T_a, T_b]\}$, where the lower and upper bounds on the sample size (T_a and T_b) remain to be specified. The objective of the Monte Carlo is to study $\text{E}[\widehat{\alpha}]$, the finite sample mean of $\widehat{\alpha}$, which is also a conditional probability formula, as given in (14.29). The asymptotic approximation to

$$\text{E}\left[\widehat{\alpha} \mid \alpha, T\right] = G(\alpha, T).$$

is $G_a(\psi, T)$, which is α, and which reduces the component simulated to $O(T^{-1})$. Additionally, we might make use of the well-known Hurwicz (1950) bias, in which case $G_a(\psi, T)$ is $(\alpha - 2\alpha/T)$, and the simulation error is $O(T^{-2})$; see Shenton and Johnson (1965).

15.3 Experimental design, simulation, and post-simulation analysis

In practice, Monte Carlo studies are implemented in three stages: experimental design, simulation, and post-simulation analysis. These three stages formalize and generalize the analysis for distribution sampling in §14.2 above.

In experimental design, we choose the values of ψ and T for each experiment that will be simulated. For the kth of K experiments, the corresponding values are denoted (ψ_k, T_k), with $k = 1, \ldots, K$.

In simulation, for the kth experiment, M replications of the statistic τ are generated. Specifically, for the ith of M replications, we generate a set of random numbers, from which data series are generated from the DGP with parameter value and sample size (ψ_k, T_k). The statistic τ is calculated from those data, and we designate it as $\tau_{i,k}$, i.e., the value of τ for the ith replication of the kth experiment. This generation of random numbers and data and calculation of τ is carried out M times, with different random numbers each time. Because understanding the mean $E[\varphi(\tau)]$ is the objective of the Monte Carlo, we calculate the stochastic analogue to this analytical function for the kth experiment, namely:

$$\overline{\varphi}_k = M^{-1} \sum_{i=1}^{M} \varphi(\tau_{i,k}).$$

That is, we average over the Monte Carlo sample of values of $\varphi(\tau_{i,k})$, paralleling the averaging over the population of $\varphi(\tau_k)$ in the formula $E[\varphi(\tau_k)]$. As noted above, antithetic variates and control variates may offer more efficient methods for using the Monte Carlo sample $\{\tau_{i,k}, \ i = 1, \ldots, M\}$ in estimating the unknown expectation $E[\varphi(\tau_k)]$. In any case, $E[\varphi(\tau_k)]$ is estimated by some Monte Carlo estimator $(\overline{\varphi}_k, $ say) for each of the K experiments under consideration.

In post-simulation analysis, we summarize and interpret the Monte Carlo results $\{\overline{\varphi}_k, \ k = 1, \ldots, K\}$ via response surfaces. Since $\overline{\varphi}_k$ is an unbiased Monte Carlo estimator of $G(\psi_k, T_k)$ (or equivalently, of $E[\varphi(\tau_k)]$), we have:

$$\overline{\varphi}_k = G(\psi_k, T_k) + \omega_k, \quad k = 1, \ldots, K,$$

where ω_k is the Monte Carlo sampling error from estimating $G(\psi_k, T_k)$ with $\overline{\varphi}_k$, and $\mathcal{E}[\overline{\varphi}_k] = G(\psi_k, T_k)$, so $\mathcal{E}[\omega_k] = 0$. Equivalently:

$$\overline{\varphi}_k - G_a(\psi_k, T_k) = G_f(\psi_k, T_k) + \omega_k \ \text{ for } k = 1, \ldots, K.$$

While $G_f(\psi_k, T_k)$ is an unknown function by assumption, its arguments ψ_k and T_k are known. Thus, some polynomial approximation of $G_f(\psi_k, T_k)$ $[H_f(\psi_k, T_k)$, say] can be estimated from this equation, and that approximation is called a response surface.

Three main issues arise in estimating response surfaces: the heteroscedasticity of ω_k across k, the statistical adequacy of the response surface, and the numerical accuracy of the response surface. These issues are addressed in the following three sub-sections, after which specific formulations of response surfaces are considered for the first and second moments of estimators, for estimated standard errors, and for test rejection frequencies. Before doing so, we illustrate the issues of design, simulation, and post-simulation analysis with the Monte Carlo simulations of the AR(1) process mentioned in Hendry (1984).

Example AR(1) process *(continued)*

In experimental design, pairs of values (α_k, T_k) are chosen. Specifically, Hendry (1984), (p. 965) chooses a full factorial design for (i.e., all possible combinations of) $\alpha = (0. \pm 0.3, \pm 0.6, \pm 0.9)$ and $T = (10, 20, 30, 40)$, yielding 28 experiments total. While σ is a design parameter as well, the experiments are invariant to σ, so Hendry set $\sigma = 1$ without loss of generality. See §14.4 below on invariance. In simulation, series of independent normal random numbers $\{\epsilon_{i,k,t}\}$ are generated, from which the $\{y_{i,k,t}\}$ are obtained via the specification of the DGP. The OLS estimates $\{\widetilde{\alpha}_{i,k}\}$ of α are calculated from the $\{y_{i,k,t}\}$, and averages of $\widetilde{\alpha}_{i,k}$ over replications $\{\overline{\alpha}_k\}$ are found. In post-simulation analysis, the estimated bias (i.e., $\overline{\alpha}_k - \alpha$) was explained as a polynomial in α_k and T_k:

$$\overline{\alpha}_k - \alpha_k = -1.84\alpha_k/(T_k + 2) + 43\alpha_k^3/T_k^3,$$

where the numerical coefficients were obtained by least squares with correction for heteroscedasticity.

15.4 Heteroscedasticity

In general, the Monte Carlo sampling error is heteroscedastic across experiments k. To correct for that heteroscedasticity, the response surface is transformed such that the new disturbance w_k (say) is distributed with constant unit variance when the equation is correctly specified. For estimators, their standard errors, and such, this is usually accomplished by weighted least squares, where the weights are inversely proportional to the Monte Carlo sampling standard deviation of $\varphi(\tau_{i,k})$ over replications. However, while response surfaces for test rejection frequencies could use similarly constructed weights, their response surfaces typically use the logistic transformation to address heteroscedasticity: see §15.7 below.

The solution to the heteroscedasticity of w_k is simple, and involves two steps. First, because we have M replications for the kth experiment, the natural Monte Carlo estimator of the variance of $\varphi(\tau_{ik})$ is:

$$V\left[\varphi\left(\tau_{i,k}\right)\right] = (M - 1)^{-1} \sum_{i=1}^{M} \left[\varphi\left(\tau_{i,k}\right) - \overline{\varphi}_k\right]^2,$$

since $G(\psi_k, T_k)$ is constant across i, for a given k. As above, $V[\cdot]$ denotes the variance with respect to the random variables in the Monte Carlo. From the discussion on distribution sampling, this estimator of the variance is unbiased, and is consistent as $M \to \infty$, provided the variance exists. Second, because:

$$V[\omega_k] = V[\overline{\varphi}_k] = V[\varphi(\tau_{i,k})]/M,$$

the estimator of the variance of ω_k is:

$$(S_k^*)^2 \equiv V[\omega_k] = M^{-1}\left\{(M-1)^{-1}\sum_{i=1}^{M}[\varphi(\tau_{i,k}) - \overline{\varphi}_k]^2\right\}.$$

Thus, the weighted response function is:

$$\overline{\varphi}_k/S_k^* = G(\psi_k, T_k)/S_k^* + \omega_k \text{ for } k = 1, \ldots, K,$$

where $\omega_k = w_k/S_k^*$ and ω_k is approximately N[0, 1] for a large number of replications M. With a partial analytical solution, the response function is:

$$[\overline{\varphi}_k - G_a(\psi_k, T_k)]/S_k^* = G_f(\psi_k, T_k)/S_k^* + \omega_k \text{ for } k = 1, \ldots, K.$$

In practice, analytical approximations to $V[\omega_k]$ can often be obtained for large econometric sample size T. Campos (1986) discusses such approximations in general for an asymptotically normally distributed estimator. Examples are given below and in Hendry (1984) for first and second moments of the OLS estimator, and in Campos (1986) for an instrumental variables estimator of a dynamic simultaneous-equations subsystem with ARMA disturbances.

15.5 Testing the statistical adequacy of response surfaces

A response surface summarizes a possibly vast array of Monte Carlo simulations in a relatively simple formula that may account for much of the variation in $\overline{\varphi}_k$ across experiments, and may be useful for predicting at points within the parameter space of the experimental design which were not included in the simulations. Further, we may assess the degree to which a response surface statistically approximates the underlying finite-sample distribution. One primary source of information exists for inferring how 'good' a response surface is ω_k, namely:

$$\omega_k \overset{D}{\to} \mathsf{IN}[0, 1]$$

where $\overset{D}{\to}$ denotes convergence in distribution, as the number of Monte Carlo replications $M \to \infty$. Using this property of ω_k, many testable implications follow from the null hypothesis that the estimated response surface equals the unknown conditional probability formula, i.e., that $H(\cdot, \cdot) = G(\cdot, \cdot)$.

Specifically, the estimated response surface is:

$$
\begin{aligned}
\overline{\varphi}_k / S_k^* &= H\left(\psi_k, T_k\right) / S_k^* + \{[G\left(\psi_k, T_k\right) - H\left(\psi_k, T_k\right)] / S_k^* + \omega_k\} \\
&= H\left(\psi_k, T_k\right) / S_k^* + v_k \qquad\qquad (15.2)
\end{aligned}
$$

where the regression error $v_k = [G(\psi_k, T_k) - H(\psi_k, T_k)] / S_k^* + \omega_k$. Under the hypothesis of correct specification of the response surface, then $H(\cdot, \cdot) = G(\cdot, \cdot)$ and so $v_k = \omega_k$. Thus, tests of the validity of the response surface can be performed by testing that v_k has the properties of ω_k. Tests based on v_k include the following.

(a) *The error v has unit variance*: $\sigma_v^2 = 1$.

   If $H(\cdot, \cdot) \neq G(\cdot, \cdot)$, then $\sigma_v^2 > 1$ because ω_k is independent of ψ_k and T_k, and so is uncorrelated with $[G(\psi_k, T_k) - H(\psi_k, T_k)]/S_k^*$. The hypothesis $\sigma_v^2 = 1$ may be tested by noting that, under the null, the residual sum of squares from the estimated response surface is distributed as a χ^2 random variate with its degrees of freedom equal to the number of experiments less the number of response-surface regressors, provided M is large. Power under the alternative is directly related to the magnitude of $[G(\psi_k, T_k) - H(\psi_k, T_k)]^2/(S_k^*)^2$ over the experiments.

(b) *The error v does not include any terms of $O(T^{-1/2})$ involving ψ and $T^{-1/2}$.*

   By using OLS, v can not include any of the terms in the polynomial $H(\cdot, \cdot)$. However, if $H(\cdot, \cdot) \neq G(\cdot, \cdot)$, then v contains terms of a higher order in ψ and $T^{-1/2}$ than those included in $H(\cdot, \cdot)$ (cf. Maasoumi and Phillips, 1982, p. 198, and Hendry, 1982, p. 210). By initially specifying a general formulation for $H(\cdot, \cdot)$ and simplifying, one can use an F statistic to test for the presence of such factors in the vs of the final (simpler) specification.

(c) *The error v does not include any terms of $O(T^0)$ involving ψ.*

   By construction, ω_k does not. However, if $H(\cdot, \cdot) \neq G(\cdot, \cdot)$, response-surface regressors of $O(T^0)$, such as a constant term, may be 'statistically significant', thereby revealing the mis-specification of $H(\cdot, \cdot)$. Likewise, the unit coefficient on the asymptotic component $G_a(\cdot, \cdot)$ may be freely estimated and tested to be unity. This unit-coefficient hypothesis is particularly noteworthy, given the importance of asymptotics in formulating the analytical properties of the response surface.

(d) *The error v is normally distributed.*

   The validity of this hypothesis rests in part on the number of replications M per experiment, and this is under the control of the investigator.

(e) *The vs are serially independent for any ordering of experiments specified prior to simulation.*

   That follows from the independence of ω_k across experiments. If $H(\cdot, \cdot) \neq G(\cdot, \cdot)$ and experiments are ordered to be (e.g.) increasing in values of ψ and

T, terms in v involving ψ and $T^{-1/2}$ may induce serial correlation and/or reveal heteroscedasticity in the vs which is correlated with the regressors.

(f) *$H(\cdot, \cdot)$ is a function with a constant parametrization.*
Recursive least-squares and split-sample Chow tests may be helpful in detecting non-constancy. As with tests of autocorrelation, ordering of the experiments is important for achieving high power. Conversely, and in criticism of many earlier studies (including several of our own), random selection of experiments for a 'forecast' sample results in little if any power to detect mis-specification of $H(\cdot, \cdot)$.

The test for (a) is the principal test of the specification of $H(\cdot, \cdot)$. It has power against all forms of mis-specification because any mis-specification implies that $\sigma_v^2 > 1$. Remaining tests, corresponding to hypotheses (b)–(f), aim at detecting specific properties of v_k that arise under certain sorts of mis-specification of $H(\cdot, \cdot)$. Thus, in some situations, these tests may have higher power than the one for (a); but in other situations they may have little or no power. Test statistics for these hypotheses are discussed in Hendry (1995b) and are computed in PcGive. Most tests have central χ^2 or F distributions under the null hypothesis that $H(\cdot, \cdot) = G(\cdot, \cdot)$, and non-central χ^2 or F distributions under the hypothesis that $H(\cdot, \cdot) \neq G(\cdot, \cdot)$.

The extent to which (a)–(f) are not satisfied reflects the degree of approximation of the response surface to the underlying conditional probability formula, although the power of tests of (a)–(f) depends crucially on the number of replications per experiment, on the experimental design (i.e., which points in $\Psi \times T$ are examined), and on the choice of DGP and $\Psi \times T$. Specifically, from the term $[G(\psi_k, T_k) - H(\psi_k, T_k)]/S_k^*$ in v_k, it follows that power depends upon the extent and nature of the deviations between $G(\cdot, \cdot)$ and $H(\cdot, \cdot)$, and the size (or rather, smallness) of S_k^*. The importance of the latter cannot be overemphasized since, with a large enough number of replications, S_k^* can be made arbitrarily small and so any departures of $H(\cdot, \cdot)$ from $G(\cdot, \cdot)$ can be detected. Finally and relatedly, even if any of (a)–(f) are rejected, the response surface still has certain desirable properties as an approximation to the unknown function $G(\cdot, \cdot)$ (see White, 1980a, pp. 155–157), and it still may account for (and so summarize) much of the inter-experimental variation.

15.6 Numerical accuracy of response surfaces

While the statistical adequacy of response surfaces depends upon the properties of the rescaled error v_k, the numerical accuracy of response surfaces turns upon the magnitude of the unscaled response surface error v_k^* (say), which is:

$$
\begin{aligned}
v_k^* &= \overline{\varphi}_k - H(\psi_k, T_k) \\
&= [\overline{\varphi}_k - G(\psi_k, T_k)] + [G(\psi_k, T_k) - H(\psi_k, T_k)]. \tag{15.3}
\end{aligned}
$$

From the second equality, the error v_k^* is composed of the degree to which the unbiased Monte Carlo estimator $\overline{\varphi}_k$ deviates from $G(\cdot,\cdot)$, plus the degree to which $H(\cdot,\cdot)$ fails to approximate $G(\cdot,\cdot)$. Thus, $G(\cdot,\cdot)$ is being approximated by simulation at given points in the parameter space, and by regression across points in the parameter space, resulting in two sources of error.

Numerical and statistical accuracy need not coincide. Specifically, for an experimental design with a large number of replications M per experiment, and so small S_k^*, the sampling error ω_k^* will be small, with the numerical error v_k^* being comprised primarily of any discrepancy between $H(\cdot,\cdot)$ and $G(\cdot,\cdot)$. That discrepancy might be very small (say 10^{-10}), yet it would be statistically significant for a large enough M (and so small enough ω_k^*). Conversely, if very few replications per experiment are generated, the tests of mis-specification will have little power to detect even numerically large discrepancies between $H(\cdot,\cdot)$ and $G(\cdot,\cdot)$. In essence, the tests of mis-specification depend upon the excess of $\mathcal{E}[(v_k^*)^2]$ over $\mathcal{E}[(\omega_k^*)^2]$. To the extent that the latter expectation is large or small, that 'excess' will be difficult or easy to detect for a given mis-specification. By contrast, numerical accuracy depends upon $\mathcal{E}[(v_k^*)^2]$ alone.

Unsurprisingly, methods for summarizing numerical and statistical accuracy may differ as well. Since numerical accuracy focuses on the size of v_k^*, summary measures such as the mean squared error of v_k^* are useful. More generally, graphs of $H(\psi_k, T_k)$ and $\overline{\varphi}_k$ across experiments can portray the ability (or lack thereof) of response surfaces to approximate $G(\psi_k, T_k)$. For examples of graphical presentation of Monte Carlo results, see Campos (1986), Ericsson (1986, 1991), and Hendry and Neale (1987).

15.7 Response surface formulations

While the specific heteroscedasticity-correction factor differs from one response surface to another, the solution above using the sampling standard deviation is generic. This section examines heteroscedasticity corrections and approximations thereto for several important cases: the first and second moments of estimators, the estimated standard errors, and test rejection frequencies. This subsection finishes with a few observations on simpler forms of response surfaces. See Hendry (1984), Campos (1986), and Ericsson (1986) for development and exposition of many of the results below.

15.7.1 First moments

For an estimator τ, the analysis of its first moment implies $\varphi(\tau_{i,k}) = \tau_{i,k}$, from which the potential functional forms of the response surface and its heteroscedasticity corrections follow.

The functional form of $H(\psi_k, T_k)$ often looks like a Taylor-series expansion in ψ_k and $T_k^{-1/2}$ around $H(\psi_k, \infty)$ [which is also $H_a(\psi_k, T_k)$]. For many consistent estimators in stationary processes, $T_k^{1/2}(\tau_{i,k} - \tau_{0,k})$ is asymptotically distributed as $\mathsf{N}[0, \Sigma_k]$, where $\tau_{0,k}$ is the 'true' value and Σ_k is the asymptotic covariance matrix of the estimator. In such cases, $H_a(\psi_k, T_k) = \tau_{0,k}$ and the next term in the expansion is $o(T^{-1/2})$ and typically $O(T^{-1})$. Inconsistent estimators can often be rewritten as being consistent for some other value. Further, they often are asymptotically normally distributed, but with an asymptotic covariance matrix different from the one corresponding to that calculated by (e.g.) the associated computer estimation package. Nonetheless, both its asymptotic bias and its asymptotic covariance matrix are calculable functions of ψ_k, so the analysis for consistent estimators generalizes to include inconsistent ones. See Hendry (1973, 1975, 1979a) for extensive discussions.

Heteroscedasticity corrections follow from the general discussion above. Specifically:

$$\mathcal{V}[\tau_{i,k}] = (M-1)^{-1} \sum_{i=1}^{M} (\tau_{i,k} - \overline{\tau}_k)^2,$$

so the heteroscedasticity correction is:

$$S_k^* = \sqrt{\mathcal{V}[\tau_{i,k}]/M}.$$

The square root of the variance $\mathcal{V}[\tau_{i,k}]$ is called the Monte Carlo standard deviation (or MCSD) of an estimator. It is of independent interest itself and is examined in §15.7.2 below.

Asymptotic theory provides a simple analytical approximation to S_k^*. If the estimator $\tau_{i,k}$ is consistent, with $T_k^{1/2}(\tau_{i,k} - \tau_{0,k})$ asymptotically distributed as $N[0, \Sigma_k]$, then S_k^* is approximately $\sqrt{[\Sigma_k/(T_k M)]}$, and Σ_k can be calculated directly from ψ_k. This heteroscedasticity-correction factor has the advantage of simplicity, but may not be correct when finite-sample properties deviate from asymptotic ones. For the AR(1) model, the asymptotic approximation to S_k^* is $\sqrt{[(1-\alpha_k^2)/(T_k M)]}$.

15.7.2 Second moments

For an estimator τ, the analysis of its second central moment $\mathcal{V}[\tau_{i,k}]$ implies $\varphi(\tau_{i,k}) = [\tau_{i,k} - \mathcal{E}(\tau_{i,k})]^2$, so the second moment is estimated by $MCSD^2$. Response surfaces typically are formulated for the logarithm of the $MCSD^2$ rather than its level. This ensures that variances predicted by the response surface are always positive. Also, it implies that the formulation remains unchanged whether the variance or any power of it is being analyzed. For a logarithmic model of $MCSD_k^2$, the asymptotic component $H_a(\psi_k, T_k)$ is $\log(\Sigma_k/T_k)$ for a consistent, asymptotically normal estimator, as is implied by the analysis for first moments.

The heteroscedasticity correction is based upon the estimated variance of the $MCSD^2$. For a response surface with $\log(MCSD_k^2)$ as its dependent variable, the correction factor may be expressed as:

$$S_k^* = \left[\left(m_{4,k} - m_{2,k}^2\right)/M\right]^{1/2}/m_{2,k},$$

where $m_{2,k}$ and $m_{4,k}$ are the Monte Carlo sample second and fourth (central) moments of $\tau_{i,k}$. If the estimator τ is mesokurtic (zero excess kurtosis), then the correction factor simplifies to:

$$S_k^* = [2/M]^{1/2} .$$

In addition to simplicity, this factor has the advantage of not relying upon estimation of the fourth moment of τ: the standard error of that sample fourth moment may be very large.

15.7.3 Estimated standard errors

The estimated standard error (ESE) is the standard error computed for an estimated coefficient, e.g., the square root of the corresponding diagonal element in $\widehat{\sigma}^2 (\mathbf{X}'\mathbf{X})^{-1}$ for the classical regression model, in standard notation. For consistent estimators with suitably estimated covariance matrices, $T^{1/2}$ESE $\to \Sigma^{1/2}$ as $T \to \infty$. That is, the (suitably rescaled) ESE is consistent for the asymptotic standard error of the estimator. Thus, a natural response surface is (see (14.29) above):

$$\left[\log \left(T_k^{1/2}\overline{\text{ESE}}_k \right) - \log \left(\Sigma_k^{1/2} \right)\right] / S_k^* = H_f \left(\psi_k, T_k\right) / S_k^* + v_k,$$

where $\overline{\text{ESE}}_k$ is the sample mean of $\text{ESE}_{i,k}$ over replications (indexed by i), S_k^* is the heteroscedasticity correction factor for $\overline{\text{ESE}}_k$ based upon the simulation standard error of $\text{ESE}_{i,k}$, and $H_f(\psi_k, T_k)$ is the purely finite-sample portion of the response surface. Asymptotically-based simplifications of S_k^* exist, but they are highly model dependent, and so are not given here; see Hendry (1984) and Campos (1986).

For inconsistent estimators (and even some consistent ones), $T^{1/2}$ESE is not consistent for $\Sigma^{1/2}$. However, as with first moments, $T^{1/2}$ESE often can be rewritten as being consistent for some other value, i.e. $\text{plim}(T^{1/2}\text{ESE})$, which can be calculated from ψ and T. A similar analysis applies to the MCSD of an inconsistent estimator. See Hendry (1979a, 1982) and Maasoumi and Phillips (1982) for examples with the MCSD, ESE, and estimated equation standard error ($\widehat{\sigma}$ in standard notation) for inconsistent estimators.

15.7.4 Test rejection frequencies

For an estimator τ, the analysis of rejection frequencies for a test based on τ implies $\varphi(\tau) = 1$ for $|\tau| > \delta$ and $\varphi(\tau) = 0$ otherwise, where δ is the two-sided critical value of the test. The function $\varphi(\tau)$ is a binary variable and $G(\cdot, \cdot)$ lies in the unit interval, which suggests using a logistic transformation of $\overline{\varphi}_k$ in the response surface as noted in §14.5 above. To simplify notation, we omit the subscript k (for the kth experiment) unless ambiguity would result; and to keep with a commonly-used notation for power functions, π and π_T are used in place of G_T, emphasizing the context of power. For examples of the analysis of rejection frequencies, see Mizon and Hendry (1980), Ericsson (1986), and Hendry and Neale (1991).

Cox (1970), (Chs. 3 and 6), in his discussion of the empirical logistic transform, provides the basis for developing response surfaces of estimated finite-sample probabilities, including both estimated finite-sample powers and estimated finite-sample probabilities of type I error. Consider a binary response variable for which the probability of 'success' (or, later, acceptance or rejection by a particular test) is π ($0 < \pi < 1$) and on which there are M observations ($M > 1$), S being the number of 'successes'. Letting:

$$A = S(M - S)/(M - 1),$$

$$\mathcal{L}(\zeta) = A^{1/2} \log\left[\zeta/(1 - \zeta)\right], \ \ 0 < \zeta < 1,$$

and, for $(2M)^{-1} < \zeta < 1 - (2M)^{-1}$:

$$\mathcal{L}^*(\zeta) = A^{1/2} \log\left[\frac{\zeta - (2M)^{-1}}{1 - \zeta - (2M)^{-1}}\right],$$

it can be shown that:

$$\mathcal{L}^*(s) - \mathcal{L}(\pi) \overset{D}{\to} \mathrm{N}\left[0, 1\right],$$

where $s \equiv S/M$, and $A^{1/2}$ parallels $(S_k^*)^{-1}$ in the general response surfaces. Thus, the logistic transformation addresses both the heteroscedasticity and the finite range of s. In the context of Monte Carlo studies of power, M is the number of replications in a particular experiment, S the number of replications for which the value of the test statistic lies in the critical region, π the finite sample (i.e., finite econometric sample T) probability of the test statistic lying in the critical region, and s the observed finite-sample rejection frequency. Below, π is treated as if it were 'power', although the analysis applies equally for size, and assumes the actual size equals the nominal.

The logistic function may be partitioned into asymptotic and finite sample components in much the way that $G(\cdot, \cdot)$ was partitioned into $G_a(\cdot, \cdot)$ and $G_f(\cdot, \cdot)$ above. Specifically:

$$\log\left[\frac{\pi_T}{1 - \pi_T}\right] = \log\left[\frac{\pi_a}{1 - \pi_a}\right] + G_f^+(\psi, T),$$

without loss of generality, where π ($\equiv \mathcal{E}[S/M]$) is subscripted by T so as to emphasize that it is a function of the econometric sample size, π_a is the (local) asymptotic (i.e., as $T \to \infty$) power of the test, and $G_f^+(\psi, T)$ is some appropriate function. On the last, $G_f^+(\psi, T)$ is the analogue of the finite-sample term $G_f(\psi, T)$ from above, but the former is what results from using the logistic transformation, and is specially indicated as such by a superscript plus.

Asymptotic theory also helps specify $G_f^+(\psi, T)$. By assumption:

$$\pi_T \to \pi_a \ \text{ as } \ T \to \infty,$$

so $G(\psi, T)$ is $o(1)$. This parallels the partition in the analysis of an estimator's properties between its asymptotic value (its plim) and its finite-sample bias (the deviation of the estimator's expectation in finite samples from its plim). While the functional form of $G_f^+(\psi, T)$ is open to investigation, from asymptotic theory one expects that its first term is $O(T^{-1/2})$ in an expansion in powers of $T^{-1/2}$. See Phillips (1977, p.474), Phillips (1982), and Sargan (1980a, p.1120).

By substitution, the original logistic equation for s may be rewritten as:

$$\mathcal{L}^*(s) - \mathcal{L}(\pi_a) = A^{1/2} G_f^+(\psi, T) + w \text{ where } w \sim \mathsf{N}[0, 1],$$

which provides a stochastic relationship between the feasible and unbiased estimator s of the actual finite-sample power, the known quantities ψ and T, and the asymptotic power π_a, which is a function of ψ and T, and can be calculated by asymptotic analysis. The error w is analogous to the error w_k in the general formulation of response surfaces. That leads to the estimated response surface:

$$\mathcal{L}^*(s) - \mathcal{L}(\pi_a) = A^{1/2} H_f^+(\psi, T) + v,$$

where $H_f^+(\psi, T)$ is the weighted least squares approximation to $G_f^+(\psi, T)$, and the error term v is the combination of w and $A^{1/2}[G_f^+(\psi, T) - H_f^+(\psi, T)]$ (the error from approximating $G_f^+\psi, T)$ by $H_f^+(\psi, T)$). Again, this parallels the general analysis of response surfaces above.

15.8 Simpler forms of response surfaces

Rather than using the possibly transformed, heteroscedasticity-corrected $\overline{\varphi}_k$ as the dependent variable, response surfaces could be estimated for $\overline{\varphi}_k$ itself:

$$\overline{\varphi}_k = H(\psi_k, T_k) + e_k,$$

where $H(\psi_k, T_k)$ is the unweighted least-squares approximation to $G(\psi_k, T_k)$ and e_k is the residual. This formulation does not account for the heteroscedasticity of $\overline{\varphi}_k$, conditional upon (ψ_k, T_k), nor does it bound the range of $H(\psi_k, T_k)$. For instance, for some values of ψ_k and T_k, $H(\psi_k, T_k)$ could be negative for variances, or lie outside the unit interval for rejection frequencies. Even so, the standard errors from White (1980b) are consistent; the response surface $H(\psi_k, T_k)$ *is* a least-squares approximation to the underlying response function $G(\psi_k, T_k)$ and has the desirable properties which that entails; and some simple response surfaces of this form can do very well as numerical approximations to the conditional expectation, and so as summaries of a large number of simulations.

Another simplification of response surfaces is to use only the asymptotic (or analytically known) component, i.e., letting $H(\psi_k, T_k) = H_a(\psi_k, T_k)$. In this case, no response surface estimation is required and the primary issues are the statistical adequacy and numerical accuracy of asymptotics. See Hendry (1973), Nickell (1981), and Ericsson (1986) for examples.

15.9 Conclusion

We will not investigate the response surface avenue further. The reader interested in greater detail is referred to Hendry (1984). Nevertheless, we stress the importance of good summarization of experiments so as to reduce the consumption costs for readers.

Chapter 16

Asymptotic Analysis

16.1 Introduction

Asymptotic analysis can form an important complement to Monte Carlo analysis. In stationary processes, population second moments can be obtained, from which probability limits of estimators and standard errors can be derived. Often, most of the variation between different values for design variables in a simulation can be explained by these asymptotic outcomes: for examples, see Hendry (1973, 1979a, 1982).

After providing the expression for the companion form of a stationary linear dynamic system, the algebra of such moment calculations is described in §16.4. Then §16.5 applies these to calculate the asymptotic moments and population statistics of regressions estimated by least squares (OLS) or instrumental variables (IV) from the general stationary linear dynamic stochastic process, for correctly-specified and misspecified models. A numerical example is used to illustrate the computations. Section 16.5.3 discusses the methods and approximations behind power calculations.

16.2 The DGP for asymptotic analysis

The basic data generation process (DGP) for the asymptotic analysis is:

$$
\begin{aligned}
\mathbf{D}\mathbf{y}_t &= \mathbf{A}_1\mathbf{y}_{t-1} + \mathbf{A}_2\mathbf{z}_t + \mathbf{a}_3 + \mathbf{A}_5\mathbf{y}_{t-2} + \mathbf{u}_t, & \mathbf{D} &= \mathbf{I}_n - \mathbf{A}_0, \\
\mathbf{u}_t &= \mathbf{B}_0\mathbf{u}_{t-1} + \mathbf{e}_t, & \mathbf{e}_t &\sim \mathsf{IN}_n\left[\mathbf{0}, \mathbf{E}_1\right], \\
\mathbf{z}_t &= \mathbf{C}_0\mathbf{z}_{t-1} + \mathbf{c}_1 + \mathbf{v}_t, & \mathbf{v}_t &\sim \mathsf{IN}_n\left[\mathbf{0}, \mathbf{E}_2\right],
\end{aligned} \tag{16.1}
$$

where $\operatorname{corr}[\mathbf{e}_t\mathbf{v}_s'] = \mathbf{0} \; \forall t \neq s$. The vectors $\mathbf{y}_t, \mathbf{u}_t, \mathbf{e}_t$ are $n \times 1$, so that the coefficient matrices $\mathbf{A}_0, \mathbf{A}_1, \mathbf{B}_0$ are $n \times n$, and $\mathbf{a}_3$ is $n \times 1$. The $\mathbf{z}_t$ vector is $q \times 1$, making $\mathbf{a}_2$ $n \times q$, $\mathbf{C}_0$ $q \times q$, and $\mathbf{c}_1$ $q \times 1$.

The vector $\mathbf{y}_t$ is determined by a multivariate endogenous process in (16.1), whereas $\mathbf{z}_t$ is strongly exogenous, and is determined by a vector autoregression (VAR). Further,

(16.1) generates a vector autoregressive error on the dynamic system, where $\mathbf{B}_0 = 0$ is admissible. The matrix $\mathbf{A}_0$ may also be zero, and the matrices $\mathbf{E}_1$ and $\mathbf{E}_2$ must be symmetric, positive definite. Finally, for asymptotic calculations, the error processes are always assumed to be normal, and the system as a whole must be stationary: §16.3 discusses the relevant conditions.

The value of every parameter in (16.1) must be defined to complete the DGP. From the parameter values thus input, and subject to the stationarity conditions noted below, asymptotic analysis means calculating the population second moments of the variables $(\mathbf{y}'_t : \mathbf{y}'_{t-1} : \mathbf{y}'_{t-2} : \mathbf{z}'_t) = \mathbf{x}'_t$ from the DGP as a whole, using the approach described in §16.4. Since the probability limits (plims) of linear econometric estimators including OLS and IV, and of statistics derived therefrom (such as estimated coefficient and equation standard errors), are functions of these population second moments, numerical values for coefficient and standard error inconsistencies can be calculated. This is shown in §16.5.

Finally, asymptotic analysis also allows the asymptotic powers of test statistics to be calculated for local alternatives, using central χ^2 approximations to non-central $\chi^2 s$, as discussed in §16.5.3.

16.2.1 An illustration

To illustrate the issues of this chapter, we use a bivariate DGP: a dynamic system for *Ya* and *Yb*. The equation of interest links Ya_t to Yb_t and Ya_{t-1} with coefficients 0.5 and 0.5 respectively, but it also has an untreated first-order autoregressive error of -0.6. The equation determining Yb_t is a partial adjustment to Za_t, with coefficients of 0.8 and 1.0, where Za_t is simply an autoregression with coefficient 0.75. All of the error variances are unity, and the covariances 0.2; all intercepts are also zero:

$$\begin{pmatrix} Ya \\ Yb \end{pmatrix}_t = \begin{pmatrix} 0 & 0.5 \\ 0 & 0 \end{pmatrix} \begin{pmatrix} Ya \\ Yb \end{pmatrix}_t + \begin{pmatrix} 0.5 & 0 \\ 0 & 0.8 \end{pmatrix} \begin{pmatrix} Ya \\ Yb \end{pmatrix}_{t-1} + \begin{pmatrix} 0 \\ 1 \end{pmatrix} Za_t + \mathbf{u}_t,$$

$$\begin{pmatrix} Ua \\ Ub \end{pmatrix}_t = \mathbf{u}_t = \begin{pmatrix} -0.6 & 0 \\ 0 & 0 \end{pmatrix} \begin{pmatrix} Ua \\ Ub \end{pmatrix}_{t-1} + \mathbf{e}_t, \quad \mathbf{e}_t \sim \text{IN} \left[0, \begin{pmatrix} 1 & 0.2 \\ 0.2 & 1 \end{pmatrix} \right],$$

$$Za_t = 0.75 Za_{t-1} + \mathbf{v}_t, \quad \mathbf{v}_t \sim \text{IN} \left[0, 1 \right].$$

16.3 Companion form

Since the basic DGP for asymptotic analysis assumes both weak and strict stationarity, the population first and second moments are well defined and relatively easy to obtain. From (16.1) above, a 'companion form' representation can be obtained by stacking all of the data variables and the corresponding coefficient matrices. At each observation t, the variables are collected in a long vector $x'_t = (y'_t : y'_{t-1} : y'_{t-2} : z'_t)$. The DGP matrices and vectors of parameters are: $\{D\ A_1\ A_2\ a_3\ A_5\ B_0\ C_0\ c_1\ c_2\ E_1\ E_2\}$. These completely characterize the DGP.

Let vec$A$ denote the column vector consisting of the stacked columns of A of a matrix $A = (a_1 \ldots a_n)$ given by:

$$\text{vec}A = \begin{pmatrix} a_1 \\ \vdots \\ a_n \end{pmatrix}.$$

We also need the operator, $\otimes$, called the Kronecker or direct product, of two matrices defined by:

$$A \otimes B = (a_{i,j}B).$$

The key operation used below for matrices which commute appropriately, and which can be verified by an element by element comparison, is the following:

$$\text{vec}(ABC) = (C' \otimes A)\,\text{vec}B. \tag{16.2}$$

The variation-free elements of:

$$\{D\ A_1\ A_2\ a_3\ A_5\ B_0\ C_0\ c_1\ c_2\ E_1 E_2\}$$

(where only the upper triangles of E_1 and E_2, including their diagonals, are retained) can be vectorized in one long vector, which we denote by θ. Then the (zero mean) DGP is fully described by θ.

The reduced, or solved form, of (16.1) is (for non-singular D):

$$\begin{aligned} y_t &= D^{-1}A_1 y_{t-1} + D^{-1}A_2 z_t + D^{-1}a_3 + D^{-1}A_5 y_{t-2} + u_t \\ &= \Pi_1 y_{t-1} + \Pi_2 z_t + \mu^* + \Pi_5 y_{t-2} + w_t \end{aligned} \tag{16.3}$$

Then, from the second equation of (16.1), on pre-multiplying by D^{-1} we have:

$$w_t = Rw_{t-1} + \varepsilon_t, \tag{16.4}$$

where $\varepsilon_t = D^{-1}e_t$, and:

$$R = D^{-1}B_0 D.$$

Combining (16.3) and (16.4):

$$\begin{aligned} y_t - \Pi_1 y_{t-1} - \Pi_2 z_t - \mu^* - \Pi_5 y_{t-2} = \\ R(y_{t-1} - \Pi_1 y_{t-2} - \Pi_2 z_{t-1} - \mu^* - \Pi_5 y_{t-3}) + \varepsilon_t, \end{aligned}$$

so collecting terms:

$$\begin{aligned} y_t &= (\Pi_1 + R)\,y_{t-1} + (\Pi_5 - R\Pi_1)\,y_{t-2} \\ &\quad - R\Pi_5 y_{t-3} + \Pi_2 z_t - R\Pi_2 z_{t-1} + (I_n - R)\,\mu^* + \varepsilon_t. \end{aligned} \tag{16.5}$$

Given the other assumptions in (16.1), stationarity requires that all of the eigenvalues of $\mathbf{C}_0$ and of the polynomial in the (lag) operator L:

$$
\begin{aligned}
\left| \mathbf{I}_n - (\mathbf{\Pi}_1 + \mathbf{R})L - (\mathbf{\Pi}_5 - \mathbf{R}\mathbf{\Pi}_1)\,L^2 + \mathbf{R}\mathbf{\Pi}_5 L^3 \right| &= \\
\left| \mathbf{I}_n - \mathbf{R}L \right| \left| \mathbf{I}_n - \mathbf{\Pi}_1 L - \mathbf{\Pi}_5 L^2 \right| &= 0
\end{aligned}
\tag{16.6}
$$

lie inside the unit circle (although this is not sufficient), where the second equality reveals that the eigenvalues of the reduced forms of (16.1) separately must all have moduli less than unity. This requirement is easily established numerically from the companion form matrix, as described below.

In terms of the original parameters of (16.1), (16.5) can be written as:

$$
\begin{aligned}
\mathbf{y}_t &= \mathbf{D}^{-1}\left(\mathbf{A}_1 + \mathbf{B}_0\mathbf{D}\right)\mathbf{y}_{t-1} + \mathbf{D}^{-1}\left(\mathbf{A}_5 - \mathbf{B}_0\mathbf{A}_1\right)\mathbf{y}_{t-2} - \mathbf{D}^{-1}\mathbf{B}_0\mathbf{A}_5\mathbf{y}_{t-3} \\
&\quad + \mathbf{D}^{-1}\mathbf{A}_2\mathbf{z}_t - \mathbf{D}^{-1}\mathbf{B}_0\mathbf{A}_2\mathbf{z}_{t-1} + \left(\mathbf{I}_n - \mathbf{D}^{-1}\mathbf{B}_0\mathbf{D}\right)\mu^* + \mathbf{D}^{-1}\mathbf{e}_t
\end{aligned}
\tag{16.7}
$$

Eliminating $\mathbf{z}_t$ in terms of $\mathbf{z}_{t-1}$ using (16.1), and stacking the four original variables $(\mathbf{y}'_t : \mathbf{y}'_{t-1} : \mathbf{y}'_{t-2} : \mathbf{z}'_t)$ in $\mathbf{x}'_t$ creates the required companion form given by the following equation:

$$
\begin{pmatrix} \mathbf{y}_t \\ \mathbf{y}_{t-1} \\ \mathbf{y}_{t-2} \\ \mathbf{z}_t \end{pmatrix} = \mu + \mathbf{\Pi} \begin{pmatrix} \mathbf{y}_{t-1} \\ \mathbf{y}_{t-2} \\ \mathbf{y}_{t-3} \\ \mathbf{z}_{t-1} \end{pmatrix} + \begin{pmatrix} \xi_t \\ 0 \\ 0 \\ \mathbf{v}_t \end{pmatrix},
\tag{16.8}
$$

where the companion matrix $\mathbf{\Pi}$ is given by:

$$
\begin{pmatrix}
\mathbf{D}^{-1}\left(\mathbf{A}_1 + \mathbf{B}_0\mathbf{D}\right) & \mathbf{D}^{-1}\left(\mathbf{A}_5 - \mathbf{B}_0\mathbf{A}_1\right) & -\mathbf{D}^{-1}\mathbf{B}_0\mathbf{A}_5 & \mathbf{D}^{-1}\left(\mathbf{A}_2\mathbf{C}_0 - \mathbf{B}_0\mathbf{A}_2\right) \\
\mathbf{I}_n & 0 & 0 & 0 \\
0 & \mathbf{I}_n & 0 & 0 \\
0 & 0 & 0 & \mathbf{C}_0
\end{pmatrix}
$$

and where $\xi_t = \mathbf{D}^{-1}\mathbf{e}_t + \mathbf{D}^{-1}\mathbf{A}_2\mathbf{v}_t$ and:

$$
\mu = \begin{pmatrix} \mathbf{D}^{-1}\left(\mathbf{a}_3 - \mathbf{B}_0\mathbf{a}_3\right) \\ 0 \\ 0 \\ \mathbf{c}_1 \end{pmatrix}.
$$

Now we can write:

$$
\mathbf{x}_t = \mu + \mathbf{\Pi}\mathbf{x}_{t-1} + \mathbf{v}_t \quad \text{with} \quad \mathbf{v}_t \sim \text{IN}_{3n+q}\left[0, \Sigma\right],
\tag{16.9}
$$

where:

$$
\Sigma = \begin{pmatrix}
\mathbf{D}^{-1}\left(\mathbf{E}_1 + \mathbf{A}_2\mathbf{E}_2\mathbf{A}'_2\right)\mathbf{D}^{-1\prime} & 0 & 0 & \mathbf{D}^{-1}\mathbf{A}_2\mathbf{E}_2 \\
0 & 0 & 0 & 0 \\
0 & 0 & 0 & 0 \\
\mathbf{E}_2\mathbf{A}'_2\mathbf{D}^{-1\prime} & 0 & 0 & \mathbf{E}_2
\end{pmatrix}
\tag{16.10}
$$

The non-zero block of Σ, remaining after deleting the central rows and columns of zeros in (16.10), is factorized as $\mathbf{PP'}$.

The condition for stationarity can now be stated as: all of the eigenvalues λ_i of $\mathbf{\Pi}$ must be less than unity in absolute value, where the λ_i solve:

$$|\lambda\mathbf{I} - \mathbf{\Pi}| = 0.$$

This ensures the condition that all the eigenvalues of the equations of the DGP lie inside the unit circle.

16.3.1 An illustration – continued

This section continues with the example DGP. First for $\mathbf{D}$:

$$\mathbf{D} = \begin{pmatrix} 1 & -0.5 \\ 0 & 1 \end{pmatrix}, \text{ so that } \mathbf{D}^{-1} = \begin{pmatrix} 1 & 0.5 \\ 0 & 1 \end{pmatrix}.$$

The terms in the companion matrix are:

$$
\begin{aligned}
\mathbf{D}^{-1}(\mathbf{A}_1 + \mathbf{B}_0\mathbf{D}) &= \begin{pmatrix} 1 & 0.5 \\ 0 & 1 \end{pmatrix}\left[\begin{pmatrix} 0.5 & 0 \\ 0 & 0.8 \end{pmatrix} + \begin{pmatrix} -0.6 & 0 \\ 0 & 0 \end{pmatrix}\begin{pmatrix} 1 & -0.5 \\ 0 & 1 \end{pmatrix}\right] \\
&= \begin{pmatrix} -0.1 & 0.7 \\ 0 & 0.8 \end{pmatrix},
\end{aligned}
$$

$$\mathbf{D}^{-1}(\mathbf{A}_5 - \mathbf{B}_0\mathbf{A}_1) = -\begin{pmatrix} 1 & 0.5 \\ 0 & 1 \end{pmatrix}\begin{pmatrix} -0.6 & 0 \\ 0 & 0 \end{pmatrix}\begin{pmatrix} 0.5 & 0 \\ 0 & 0.8 \end{pmatrix} = \begin{pmatrix} 0.3 & 0 \\ 0 & 0 \end{pmatrix},$$

$$
\begin{aligned}
\mathbf{D}^{-1}(\mathbf{A}_2\mathbf{C}_0 - \mathbf{B}_0\mathbf{A}_2) &= \begin{pmatrix} 1 & 0.5 \\ 0 & 1 \end{pmatrix}\left[\begin{pmatrix} 0 \\ 1 \end{pmatrix}0.75 - \begin{pmatrix} -0.6 & 0 \\ 0 & 0 \end{pmatrix}\begin{pmatrix} 0 \\ 1 \end{pmatrix}\right] \\
&= \begin{pmatrix} 0.375 \\ 0.75 \end{pmatrix}.
\end{aligned}
$$

The terms in the variance matrix of the companion form are:

$$\mathbf{D}^{-1}(\mathbf{E}_1 + \mathbf{A}_2\mathbf{E}_2\mathbf{A}_2')\mathbf{D}^{-1\prime} = \begin{pmatrix} 1 & 0.5 \\ 0 & 1 \end{pmatrix}\begin{pmatrix} 1 & 0.2 \\ 0.2 & 1 \end{pmatrix}\begin{pmatrix} 1 & 1 \\ 0.5 & 1 \end{pmatrix} = \begin{pmatrix} 1.7 & 1.2 \\ 1.2 & 2 \end{pmatrix},$$

$$\mathbf{E}_2\mathbf{A}_2'\mathbf{D}^{-1\prime} = \begin{pmatrix} 0 & 1 \end{pmatrix}\begin{pmatrix} 1 & 0 \\ 0.5 & 1 \end{pmatrix} = \begin{pmatrix} 0.5 & 1 \end{pmatrix}$$

The complete companion form, when we allow for an extra lag, is:

$$
\begin{pmatrix} Ya_t \\ Yb_t \\ Ya_{t-1} \\ Yb_{t-1} \\ Ya_{t-2} \\ Yb_{t-2} \\ Za_t \end{pmatrix} = \begin{pmatrix} -0.1 & 0.7 & 0.3 & 0 & 0 & 0 & 0.375 \\ 0 & 0.8 & 0 & 0 & 0 & 0 & 0.75 \\ 1 & 0 & 0 & 0 & 0 & 0 & 0 \\ 0 & 1 & 0 & 0 & 0 & 0 & 0 \\ 0 & 0 & 1 & 0 & 0 & 0 & 0 \\ 0 & 0 & 0 & 1 & 0 & 0 & 0 \\ 0 & 0 & 0 & 0 & 0 & 0 & 0.75 \end{pmatrix}\begin{pmatrix} Ya_{t-1} \\ Yb_{t-1} \\ Ya_{t-2} \\ Yb_{t-2} \\ Ya_{t-3} \\ Yb_{t-3} \\ Za_{t-1} \end{pmatrix} + \nu_t, \quad (16.11)
$$

with:

$$\boldsymbol{\Sigma} = \begin{pmatrix} 1.7 & 1.2 & 0 & 0 & 0 & 0 & 0.5 \\ 1.2 & 2 & 0 & 0 & 0 & 0 & 1 \\ 0 & 0 & 0 & 0 & 0 & 0 & 0 \\ 0 & 0 & 0 & 0 & 0 & 0 & 0 \\ 0 & 0 & 0 & 0 & 0 & 0 & 0 \\ 0 & 0 & 0 & 0 & 0 & 0 & 0 \\ 0.5 & 1 & 0 & 0 & 0 & 0 & 1 \end{pmatrix}. \tag{16.12}$$

16.4 Asymptotic moments

Assuming that stationarity holds, then the long-run mean of $\mathbf{y}_t$ is obtained by taking expected values in (16.5), noting that the expected value of $\mathbf{z}_t$ from (16.1) is:

$$\mathsf{E}\left[\mathbf{z}_t\right] = \left(\mathbf{I}_m - \mathbf{C}_0\right)^{-1}\mathbf{c}_1 = \mathbf{c}. \tag{16.13}$$

Consequently, since $\mathsf{E}[\mathbf{y}_t] = \mathsf{E}[\mathbf{y}_{t-1}]$ etc. we obtain from (16.5):

$$\begin{aligned} \mathsf{E}\left[\mathbf{y}_t\right] &= \left(\boldsymbol{\Pi}_1 + \mathbf{R}\right)\mathsf{E}\left[\mathbf{y}_t\right] + \left(\boldsymbol{\Pi}_5 - \mathbf{R}\boldsymbol{\Pi}_1\right)\mathsf{E}\left[\mathbf{y}_t\right] - \mathbf{R}\boldsymbol{\Pi}_5\mathsf{E}\left[\mathbf{y}_t\right] \\ &\quad + \boldsymbol{\Pi}_2\mathsf{E}\left[\mathbf{z}_t\right] - \mathbf{R}\boldsymbol{\Pi}_2\mathsf{E}\left[\mathbf{z}_t\right] + \left(\mathbf{I}_n - \mathbf{R}\right)\boldsymbol{\mu}^*. \end{aligned}$$

or:

$$\mathsf{E}\left[\mathbf{y}_t\right] = \left[\mathbf{I}_n - \boldsymbol{\Pi}_1 - \mathbf{R} + \boldsymbol{\Pi}_5 - \mathbf{R}\boldsymbol{\Pi}_1 + \mathbf{R}\boldsymbol{\Pi}_5\right]^{-1}\left[\left(\mathbf{I}_n - \mathbf{R}\right)\left(\boldsymbol{\Pi}_2\mathbf{c} + \boldsymbol{\mu}^*\right)\right] = \boldsymbol{\eta}. \tag{16.14}$$

An interesting implication of (16.14) is that $\mathsf{E}[\mathbf{y}_t]$ does not depend on $\mathbf{B}_0$, since, as in (16.6):

$$\mathbf{I}_n - \boldsymbol{\Pi}_1 - \mathbf{R} + \boldsymbol{\Pi}_5 - \mathbf{R}\boldsymbol{\Pi}_1 + \mathbf{R}\boldsymbol{\Pi}_5 = \left(\mathbf{I}_n - \mathbf{R}\right)\left(\mathbf{I}_n - \boldsymbol{\Pi}_1 - \boldsymbol{\Pi}_5\right),$$

and hence $(\mathbf{I}_n - \mathbf{R})$ factors out of (16.14):

$$\mathsf{E}\left[\mathbf{y}_t\right] = \left(\mathbf{I}_n - \boldsymbol{\Pi}_1 - \boldsymbol{\Pi}_5\right)^{-1}\left(\boldsymbol{\Pi}_2\mathbf{c} + \boldsymbol{\mu}^*\right) = \boldsymbol{\eta}. \tag{16.15}$$

In terms of the original matrices:

$$\left(\mathbf{D} - \mathbf{A}_1 - \mathbf{A}_5\right)^{-1}\left[\mathbf{A}_2\left(\mathbf{I}_q - \mathbf{C}_0\right)^{-1}\mathbf{c}_1 + \mathbf{a}_3\right] = \boldsymbol{\eta}$$

This result confirms one's intuition, but also points towards the possible dangers of trying to capture the dynamics of behavioural relationships using autocorrelated errors unless the residual autocorrelation is genuinely due to error autocorrelation.

In the remainder we assume that $\mathsf{E}[\mathbf{x}_t] = \mathbf{0}$ for simplicity, thus setting $\mathbf{a}_3$ and $\mathbf{c}_1$, and hence $\boldsymbol{\mu}$ to zero. However, the analysis can be generalized to allow for intercepts, using the long-run mean $\boldsymbol{\gamma}' = (\boldsymbol{\eta}' \ \boldsymbol{\eta}' \ \boldsymbol{\eta}' \ \mathbf{c}')$ then working with the deviations $(\mathbf{x}_t - \boldsymbol{\gamma})$

from that mean. In the zero-mean case, the population second-moment matrix of x_t is denoted by:

$$E\left[x_t x_t'\right] = M.$$

From the structure of (16.9), and using the fact that:

$$E\left[x_{t-1} \nu_t'\right] = 0 \text{ whereas } E\left[x_t \nu_t'\right] = \Sigma,$$

then the asymptotic moments of x_t can be obtained by post-multiplying (16.9) by x_t' and x_{t-1}' respectively, and taking expectations to yield:

$$E\left[x_t x_t'\right] = M = \Pi E\left[x_{t-1} x_t'\right] + E\left[\nu_t x_t'\right] = \Pi M_1' + \Sigma, \tag{16.16}$$

and:

$$E\left[x_t x_{t-1}'\right] = M_1 = \Pi M. \tag{16.17}$$

Substituting the transpose of M_1 from (16.17) in (16.16):

$$M = \Pi M \Pi' + \Sigma. \tag{16.18}$$

This somewhat non-standard equation in M as a function of $(\Pi : \Sigma)$ can be solved using (16.2):

$$\text{vec} M = (\Pi \otimes \Pi) \text{vec} M + \text{vec} \Sigma,$$

so that:

$$\text{vec} M = (I - \Pi \otimes \Pi)^{-1} \text{vec} \Sigma. \tag{16.19}$$

Thus, M only depends on the value of θ, the parameters of the DGP (16.1), and can therefore be calculated numerically once these are fully specified.

Given M, then M_1 is obtained from (16.17). It is useful to record their structure, namely:

$$M = \begin{pmatrix} E\left[y_t y_t'\right] & E\left[y_t y_{t-1}'\right] & E\left[y_t y_{t-2}'\right] & E\left[y_t z_t'\right] \\ E\left[y_{t-1} y_t'\right] & E\left[y_{t-1} y_{t-1}'\right] & E\left[y_{t-1} y_{t-2}'\right] & E\left[y_{t-1} z_t'\right] \\ E\left[y_{t-2} y_t'\right] & E\left[y_{t-2} y_{t-1}'\right] & E\left[y_{t-2} y_{t-2}'\right] & E\left[y_{t-2} z_t'\right] \\ E\left[z_t y_t'\right] & E\left[z_t y_{t-1}'\right] & E\left[z_t y_{t-2}'\right] & E\left[z_t z_t'\right] \end{pmatrix} \tag{16.20}$$

and:

$$M_1 = \begin{pmatrix} E\left[y_t y_{t-1}'\right] & E\left[y_t y_{t-2}'\right] & E\left[y_t y_{t-3}'\right] & E\left[y_t z_{t-1}'\right] \\ E\left[y_{t-1} y_{t-1}'\right] & E\left[y_{t-1} y_{t-2}'\right] & E\left[y_{t-1} y_{t-3}'\right] & E\left[y_{t-1} z_{t-1}'\right] \\ E\left[y_{t-3} y_{t-1}'\right] & E\left[y_{t-3} y_{t-2}'\right] & E\left[y_{t-3} y_{t-3}'\right] & E\left[y_{t-3} z_{t-1}'\right] \\ E\left[z_t y_{t-1}'\right] & E\left[z_t y_{t-2}'\right] & E\left[z_t y_{t-3}'\right] & E\left[z_t z_{t-1}'\right] \end{pmatrix} \tag{16.21}$$

Thus, all the possible second moments can be found within one of these two $(3n+q) \times (3n+q)$ matrices.

16.4.1 An illustration – continued

We can now compute vecM for the example, substituting Π from (16.11) and Σ from (16.12) into (16.19). The next step is to undo the vectorization to obtain M. To avoid manual computation, we created the following Ox program:

....*asymp.ox (part of)*

```
#include <oxstd.h>

main()
{
    decl pi = <
        -0.1, 0.7, 0.3,    0, 0, 0, 0.375;
           0, 0.8,   0,    0, 0, 0, 0.75 ;
         1.0,   0,   0,    0, 0, 0,    0;
           0, 1.0,   0,    0, 0, 0,    0;
           0,   0, 1.0,    0, 0, 0,    0;
           0,   0,   0,  1.0, 0, 0,    0;
           0,   0,   0,    0, 0, 0, 0.75>;
    decl cp = rows(pi);
    decl sigma = <
        1.7, 1.2, 0, 0, 0, 0, 0.5;
        1.2, 2.0, 0, 0, 0, 0, 1.0;
          0,   0, 0, 0, 0, 0,   0;
          0,   0, 0, 0, 0, 0,   0;
          0,   0, 0, 0, 0, 0,   0;
          0,   0, 0, 0, 0, 0,   0;
        0.5, 1.0, 0, 0, 0, 0, 1.0>;
    decl vecm = invert(unit(cp * cp) - pi ** pi) * vec(sigma);
    decl m = reshape(vecm, cp, cp);
    println("M", m);
}
```
....

Running this program gives:

$$
M = \begin{pmatrix}
 & Ya_t & Yb_t & Ya_{t-1} & Yb_{t-1} & Ya_{t-2} & Yb_{t-2} & Za_t \\
\hline
Ya_t & 27.104 & 26.561 & 25.138 & 26.612 & 24.177 & 25.692 & 4.5714 \\
Yb_t & 26.561 & 28.175 & 24.678 & 26.825 & 22.313 & 24.675 & 5.7143 \\
Ya_{t-1} & 25.138 & 24.678 & 27.104 & 26.561 & 25.138 & 26.612 & 3.4286 \\
Yb_{t-1} & 26.612 & 26.825 & 26.561 & 28.175 & 24.678 & 26.825 & 4.2857 \\
Ya_{t-2} & 24.177 & 22.313 & 25.138 & 24.678 & 27.104 & 26.561 & 2.5714 \\
Yb_{t-2} & 25.692 & 24.675 & 26.612 & 26.825 & 26.561 & 28.175 & 3.2143 \\
Za_t & 4.5714 & 5.7143 & 3.4286 & 4.2857 & 2.5714 & 3.2143 & 2.2857
\end{pmatrix} \tag{16.22}
$$

16.5 Asymptotic statistics

From the moment matrices in the previous section, all required functions of regression (OLS) and instrumental variables (IV) estimators can be obtained. First, we formulate the equations to be estimated and their estimators.

16.5.1 The estimators

Consider a linear equation asserted by an investigator to link a subset of the variables of x_t, where the dependent variable is denoted by p_t, the k regressor variables by q_t and the corresponding k coefficients by β such that:

$$p_t = \beta' q_t + v_t \text{ for } t = 1, \dots, T, \tag{16.23}$$

where it is also claimed that:

$$v_t \underset{h}{\sim} \text{IN}\left[0, \sigma^2\right], \tag{16.24}$$

and the symbol $\underset{h}{\sim}$ denotes 'is distributed by hypothesis as'. No assumption is made in this section that any of the investigator's assertions in (16.23) and (16.24) are true, although they may in fact be so. Collecting all the observations in the conventional matrix formulation leads to:

$$p = Q\beta + v. \tag{16.25}$$

We allow for the existence of a further subset of x_t which constitute a set of k instrumental variables, denoted by g_t (not overlapping completely with q_t), such that it is claimed:

$$E_h\left[g_t v_t\right] = 0, \tag{16.26}$$

where E_h denotes 'expectation under the hypothesis'. As before, the assertions in (16.26) need not be true.

The OLS estimators of β and σ^2, and the values of the calculated coefficient standard errors under the hypothesis that (16.24) and (16.25) hold, together with:

$$E_h\left[q_t v_t\right] = 0, \tag{16.27}$$

are given by:

$$\widehat{\beta} = \left(Q'Q\right)^{-1} Q'p, \tag{16.28}$$

and:

$$\widehat{\sigma}^2 = T^{-1}\left(p'p - p'Q\widehat{\beta}\right), \tag{16.29}$$

since $p'Q\widehat{\beta} = \widehat{\beta}' Q'Q\widehat{\beta}$ in OLS; with:

$$\widehat{V\left[\widehat{\beta}\right]} = \widehat{\sigma}^2 \left(Q'Q\right)^{-1}. \tag{16.30}$$

These expressions depend only on the second moments of the observed data, and hence their plims depend only on M, which is known from §16.4.

Similarly, the corresponding IV estimators are given by:

$$\widehat{\beta}_{\text{IV}} = \left(Q'G\left(G'G\right)^{-1} G'Q\right)^{-1} Q'G(G'G)^{-1}G'p \tag{16.31}$$

where:

$$\hat{\sigma}_{\text{IV}}^2 = T^{-1}\left(\mathbf{p}'\mathbf{p} - 2\mathbf{p}'\mathbf{Q}\hat{\beta} + \hat{\beta}'\mathbf{Q}'\mathbf{Q}\hat{\beta}\right), \tag{16.32}$$

and:

$$\widehat{\mathsf{V}\left[\hat{\beta}_{\text{IV}}\right]} = \hat{\sigma}_{\text{IV}}^2 \left(\mathbf{Q}'\mathbf{G}\left(\mathbf{G}'\mathbf{G}\right)^{-1}\mathbf{G}'\mathbf{Q}\right)^{-1}. \tag{16.33}$$

Note that the OLS formulae are special cases of those for IV obtained by setting $\mathbf{G} = \mathbf{Q}$.

The final important step is that M can be estimated consistently by the sample second moment of $\mathbf{X} = (\mathbf{x}_1 \dots \mathbf{x}_T)$:

$$\operatorname*{plim}_{T\to\infty} T^{-1}\mathbf{X}'\mathbf{X} = \mathsf{M}. \tag{16.34}$$

All of $\{\mathbf{p}_t' : \mathbf{q}_t' : \mathbf{g}_t'\}$ are a subset of $\mathbf{x}_t'$, so that:

$$\mathsf{E}\left[\mathbf{p}_t\mathbf{p}_t'\right], \ \mathsf{E}\left[\mathbf{q}_t\mathbf{q}_t'\right], \ \mathsf{E}\left[\mathbf{g}_t\mathbf{g}_t'\right], \ \mathsf{E}\left[\mathbf{p}_t\mathbf{q}_t'\right], \ \mathsf{E}\left[\mathbf{p}_t\mathbf{g}_t'\right] \ \text{and} \ \mathsf{E}\left[\mathbf{q}_t\mathbf{g}_t'\right] \tag{16.35}$$

can be obtained as selections from M. Again, their scaled sample counterparts converge in probability to the corresponding population moments.

16.5.2 The asymptotic statistics

The key feature of the present approach is that the probability limits, namely:

$$\operatorname*{plim}_{T\to\infty} \hat{\beta} = \beta_p, \ \operatorname*{plim}_{T\to\infty} \hat{\sigma}^2 = \sigma_p^2 \ \text{and} \ \operatorname*{plim}_{T\to\infty} \widehat{T\mathsf{V}\left[\hat{\beta}\right]} = \mathsf{V}_p,$$

of all the relevant statistics are based purely on M. In the remainder, let $\mathcal{S}_k$ denote a selection operator which chooses the elements $\mathbf{k}_t$ from $\mathbf{x}_t$. Then:

$$\mathbf{p}_t = \mathcal{S}_p\mathbf{x}_t; \ \mathbf{q}_t = \mathcal{S}_q\mathbf{x}_t; \ \mathbf{g}_t = \mathcal{S}_g\mathbf{x}_t.$$

First for OLS, using (16.34):

$$\operatorname*{plim}_{T\to\infty} T^{-1}\mathbf{Q}'\mathbf{Q} = \operatorname*{plim}_{T\to\infty} T^{-1}\mathcal{S}_q\mathbf{X}'\mathbf{X}\mathcal{S}_q' = \mathcal{S}_q\mathsf{M}\mathcal{S}_q'$$

and similarly for all the other second moments. Consequently:

$$\operatorname*{plim}_{T\to\infty} \hat{\beta} = \operatorname*{plim}_{T\to\infty} \left[T^{-1}\mathbf{Q}'\mathbf{Q}\right]^{-1}[T^{-1}\mathbf{Q}'\mathbf{p}] = \left(\mathcal{S}_q\mathsf{M}\mathcal{S}_q'\right)^{-1}\mathcal{S}_q\mathsf{M}\mathcal{S}_p.$$

and:

$$\operatorname*{plim}_{T\to\infty} \hat{\sigma}^2 = \operatorname*{plim}_{T\to\infty} \left(T^{-1}\mathbf{p}'\mathbf{p} - \left(T^{-1}\mathbf{p}'\mathbf{Q}\right)\hat{\beta}\right) = \left(\mathcal{S}_p'\mathsf{M}\mathcal{S}_p - \mathcal{S}_p'\mathsf{M}\mathcal{S}_q\beta_p\right),$$

and hence:

$$\plim_{T\to\infty} \widehat{TV\left[\widehat{\beta}\right]} = \sigma_p^2 \left(\mathcal{S}_q \mathbf{M} \mathcal{S}_q'\right)^{-1}.$$

More generally, for IV:

$$\plim_{T\to\infty} T^{-1}\mathbf{Q}'\mathbf{G} = \plim_{T\to\infty} T^{-1}\mathcal{S}_q \mathbf{X}'\mathbf{X}\mathcal{S}_g' = \mathcal{S}_q \mathbf{M} \mathcal{S}_g'$$

and similarly for all the other second moments. Consequently:

$$\begin{aligned}
\plim_{T\to\infty} \widehat{\beta}_{\mathrm{IV}} &= \plim_{T\to\infty} \left[\tfrac{1}{T}\mathbf{Q}'\mathbf{G}\left(\tfrac{1}{T}\mathbf{G}'\mathbf{G}\right)^{-1}\tfrac{1}{T}\mathbf{G}'\mathbf{Q}\right]^{-1}\left[\tfrac{1}{T}\mathbf{Q}'\mathbf{G}\left(\tfrac{1}{T}\mathbf{G}'\mathbf{G}\right)^{-1}\tfrac{1}{T}\mathbf{G}'\mathbf{p}\right] \\
&= \left(\mathcal{S}_q \mathbf{M} \mathcal{S}_g'\left(\mathcal{S}_g \mathbf{M} \mathcal{S}_g'\right)^{-1}\mathcal{S}_g \mathbf{M} \mathcal{S}_q'\right)^{-1}\mathcal{S}_q \mathbf{M} \mathcal{S}_g'\left(\mathcal{S}_g \mathbf{M} \mathcal{S}_g'\right)^{-1}\mathcal{S}_g \mathbf{M} \mathcal{S}_p.
\end{aligned}$$

and:

$$\begin{aligned}
\plim_{T\to\infty} \widehat{\sigma}_{\mathrm{IV}}^2 &= \plim_{T\to\infty} \left(T^{-1}\mathbf{p}'\mathbf{p} - 2\left(T^{-1}\mathbf{p}'\mathbf{Q}\right)\widehat{\beta} + \widehat{\beta}'\left(T^{-1}\mathbf{Q}'\mathbf{Q}\right)\widehat{\beta}\right) \\
&= \left(\mathcal{S}_p'\mathbf{M}\mathcal{S}_p - 2\mathcal{S}_p'\mathbf{M}\mathcal{S}_q\beta_p + \beta_p'\mathcal{S}_q\mathbf{M}\mathcal{S}_q'\beta_p\right) = \sigma_{p,\mathrm{IV}}^2,
\end{aligned}$$

and hence:

$$\plim_{T\to\infty} \widehat{TV\left[\widehat{\beta}_{\mathrm{IV}}\right]} = \sigma_{p,\mathrm{IV}}^2 \left(\mathcal{S}_q \mathbf{M} \mathcal{S}_g'\left(\mathcal{S}_g \mathbf{M} \mathcal{S}_g'\right)^{-1}\mathcal{S}_g \mathbf{M} \mathcal{S}_q'\right)^{-1}.$$

Given a numerical value for the matrix M, all of these functions are easily calculated. Note that $\mathrm{V}[\widehat{\beta}]$ will be the correct variance matrix for $\widehat{\beta}$ only if the model in (16.23) is correctly specified relative to the DGP (Hendry, 1982, provides the derivations for the general case, including mis-specified models). Once the value of M has been computed, the values of all the above functions follow for any specification of the selection operators.

16.5.3 An illustration – continued

The running DGP example of this chapter links Ya_t to Yb_t and Ya_{t-1} with coefficients 0.5 and 0.5 respectively, but it also has an first-order autoregressive error of -0.6. The equation determining Yb_t is a partial adjustment to Za_t, with coefficients of 0.8 and 1.0, where Za_t is simply an autoregression with coefficient 0.75. All of the error variances are unity, and all covariances 0.2. All intercepts are zero, and for calibrating the coefficient standard errors we take $T = 120$.

The contemporaneous moment matrix M was given in (16.22). M_1 is not reported, as it is not relevant to the remaining calculations, although it does contain information which would be essential if, say, the plim of the residual autocorrelation coefficient was desired. From M, we can calculate the plims of the econometric estimators etc.

Selecting the regressors can be implemented in two ways (remember that indexing in Ox start at zero):

$$\begin{pmatrix} 0 & 1 & 1 & 0 & 0 & 0 & 0 \end{pmatrix} M \begin{pmatrix} 0 \\ 1 \\ 1 \\ 0 \\ 0 \\ 0 \\ 0 \end{pmatrix} \quad \text{or} \quad M[1\ 2][1\ 2].$$

The code uses the latter:

....*asymp.ox (part of)*

```
estimate(const mM, const asM, const vSelY, const vSelQ, const vSelG,
    const cT)
{
    // --------- OLS
    decl qq = mM[vSelQ][vSelQ];
    decl qq_inv = invertsym(qq);
    decl qy = mM[vSelQ][vSelY];
    decl beta1 = qq_inv * qy;
    decl ese1 = mM[vSelY][vSelY] - qy'beta1;
    decl bse1 = sqrt(diagonal(qq_inv)' * ese1);
    println("%r", {"OLS beta", "se[beta.T]", "se[beta]"},
            "%c", asM[vSelQ],
            beta1' | bse1' | bse1' / sqrt(cT),
            "sigma = ", sqrt(ese1));

    // --------- IVE
    decl gg_inv = invertsym(mM[vSelG][vSelG]);
    decl qg = mM[vSelQ][vSelG], gy = mM[vSelG][vSelY];
    decl qggq_inv = invertsym(qg * gg_inv * qg');
    decl qggy = qg * gg_inv * gy;
    decl beta2 = qggq_inv * qggy;
    decl ese2 = mM[vSelY][vSelY] - 2 * qy'beta2 + beta2' qq * beta2;
    decl bse2 = sqrt(diagonal(qggq_inv)' * ese2);
    println("%r", {"IVE beta", "se[beta.T]", "se[beta]"},
            "%c", asM[vSelQ],
            beta2' | bse2' | bse2' / sqrt(cT),
            "sigma = ", sqrt(ese2));

    return {beta1, bse1, beta2, bse2};
}
```
....

First results for two estimators are shown for the linear model between Ya_t and $(Yb_t : Ya_{t-1})$, namely OLS, and IV, making Yb_t endogenous and using the legitimate over-identifying instruments Yb_{t-1} and Za_t. The outcomes are:

	OLS		IV	
	Yb_t	Ya_{t-1}	Yb_t	Ya_{t-1}
β_p	0.644	0.341	0.685	0.304
$\sqrt{V_p}$	0.500	0.509	0.653	0.638
$\sqrt{(V_p/T)}$	0.046	0.046	0.060	0.058
	$\sigma_p = 1.193$		$\sigma_{p,\text{IV}} = 1.197$	

In both cases the inconsistencies are substantial at around 20%, and are due to the neglected autocorrelation. This arises because Ya_{t-1} is also treated as an instrument, but is not legitimate. However, the plims of the estimated coefficient standard errors (denoted by $\sqrt{V_p}$), are small when calibrated to $T = 120$. Even so, there is a 19% increase in σ_p from ignoring the autocorrelation, relative to the unit value in the DGP. The IV estimator is also inconsistent here, and the estimated standard errors are about 40% larger than OLS, although σ_p is estimated almost correctly.

Adding an extra lag of both variables removes the autocorrelation:[1]

	OLS				IV			
	Yb_t	Ya_{t-1}	Yb_{t-1}	Ya_{t-2}	Yb_t	Ya_{t-1}	Yb_{t-1}	Ya_{t-2}
β_p	0.585	−0.088	0.195	0.314	0.500	−0.100	0.300	0.300
$\sqrt{V_p}$	0.647	0.836	1.047	0.521	0.861	0.847	1.264	0.533
$\sqrt{(V_p/T)}$	0.059	0.076	0.096	0.048	0.079	0.077	0.115	0.049
	$\sigma_p = 0.991$				$\sigma_p = 1.000$			

The OLS coefficient inconsistencies are still present, owing to the neglected simultaneity. The IV estimator, on the other hand, is consistent here, but the estimated standard errors are about 30% larger than OLS.

---

[1] When there is no correlation between Ya and Yb, the parameters can also be estimated consistently by IV using $(Yb_t : Ya_{t-1})$ as endogenous regressors, and Yb_{t-1} and Za_t as instruments:

	OLS, $\sigma_p = 1.212$		IV, $\sigma_p = 1.250$	
	Yb_t	Ya_{t-1}	Yb_t	Ya_{t-1}
β_p	0.613	0.370	0.500	0.500
$\sqrt{V_p}$	0.502	0.515	0.722	0.755
$\sqrt{(V_p/T)}$	0.046	0.047	0.066	0.069

Note how small the change is in σ_p despite the substantial change in the parameter values.

16.5.4 Power calculations

The asymptotic power of a χ^2 test with k degrees of freedom requires the evaluation of the non-centrality parameter $\varphi > 0$ of the non-central $\chi^2(k, \varphi)$ distribution[2] (see, e.g. Johnson, Kotz and Balakrishnan, 1995). Specifically, from §16.5 (see Hendry, 1982):

$$\sqrt{T}\left(\widehat{\beta} - \beta_p\right) \sim \mathsf{N}_k\left[\mathbf{0}, \mathbf{V}\right], \tag{16.36}$$

where $\mathbf{V}$ is the correct variance matrix (consistently estimated by the Monte Carlo sampling variance, but not calculated in asymptotic analysis as yet). From (16.36), for k variables:

$$T\left(\widehat{\beta} - \beta_p\right)' \mathbf{V}^{-1} \left(\widehat{\beta} - \beta_p\right) \sim \chi^2(k). \tag{16.37}$$

Consider the (Pitman) sequence of hypothesized local alternatives β_h such that:

$$\beta_p = \beta_h + \beta^* / \sqrt{T}, \tag{16.38}$$

then from (16.37):

$$T\left(\widehat{\beta} - \beta_h\right)' \mathbf{V}^{-1} \left(\widehat{\beta} - \beta_h\right) \sim \chi^2(k, \varphi), \tag{16.39}$$

where:

$$\varphi = \beta^{*'}\mathbf{V}^{-1}\beta^* = T\left(\beta_p - \beta_h\right)' \mathbf{V}^{-1} \left(\beta_p - \beta_h\right) = T\psi. \tag{16.40}$$

Many testing problems in econometrics have this general form (see e.g. Mizon and Hendry, 1980).

Once k and φ have been determined, and a size α selected, the power function:

$$\mathsf{P}\left(\chi^2\left(k, \varphi\right) > C_\alpha \mid T\right) \tag{16.41}$$

can be graphed at each T. Note that in a restrictions test, as discussed above, the first (degrees of freedom) parameter of the non-central χ^2 is fixed. On the other hand, in Chow-type tests, the degrees of freedom are also a function of sample size. Numerical examples are given in §12.6 and in the next section.

---

[2]If the non-central χ^2 distribution is unavailable, an approximation can be found from matching the first two moments (see Hendry, 1995b, Ch. 13):

$$\chi^2\left(k, \varphi\right) \approx \left(\frac{k + 2\varphi}{k + \varphi}\right) \chi^2\left(k + \varphi\right).$$

16.5.5 An illustration – continued

As an illustration of linking the two aspects of asymptotic analysis, we can use the values of the population parameters to calibrate a calculated t-test of the hypothesis that the Yb_t coefficient is 0.5 (the true value). It must be stressed that this test is not actually t distributed because the coefficient variances are inconsistently estimated by the estimator's formula. But, to a first approximation, for the case with the autocorrelation removed, we might anticipate the IV test to reject at about its nominal size (since it is consistent, so that the non-centrality is zero asymptotically, even if the denominator is inconsistently estimated), whereas for OLS:

$$\varphi = T \left(\beta_{bp} - \tfrac{1}{2}\right)^2 / V_{bp} = 0.017T. \qquad (16.42)$$

The Ox code for this problem is:

. . . .*asymp.ox (part of)*

```
decl phi1 = sqr( (beta1[0][0]  - 0.5) / bse1[0][0] );
decl t = range(1,12) * 10;
println("asymptotic power for H0: beta=0.5, phi/T=", phi1,
    1 - probchi(quanchi(0.95,1), ones(1,12), phi1 * t));
```

. . . .

Using (16.42) yields the power function (as T increases from 10 to 120) shown in Figure 16.1. As can be seen, the 'power' rises steadily, it being important to note that the correct hypothesis (relative to the DGP) is being rejected. Simulation of this problem on PcNaive yields an empirical rejection frequency of 70% at $T = 120$.

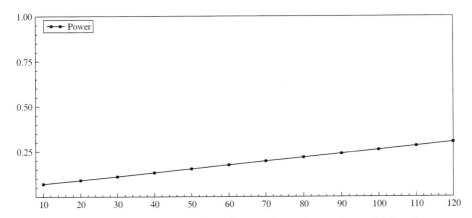

Figure 16.1 Power function for $H_0 : \beta = 0.5$ for an inconsistent OLS estimator.

Similar principles hold for testing the usual null of a zero coefficient which has a non-centrality parameter of:

$$\varphi = T\beta_{bp}^2 / V_{bp} = 1.82T \qquad (16.43)$$

The power starts high at 0.816 for $T = 10$ and rises rapidly to unity for this hypothesis. From PcNaive, the empirical rejection frequency at $T = 120$ is estimated as 1.00. The accuracy of the crude approximation is surprisingly good for such a case.

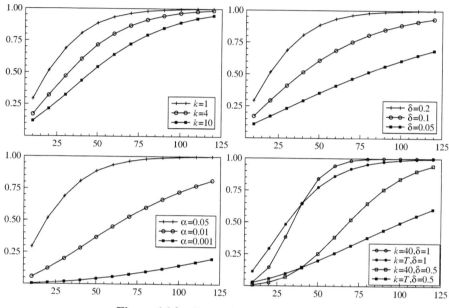

Figure 16.2   Power function behaviour.

The other main purpose of asymptotic analysis is to illustrate various facets of test behaviour. For example, Figure 16.2a shows the effect of increasing the degrees of freedom k of a type $\chi^2(k, \varphi)$ test when $\varphi = T\delta = 0.2T$ and $\alpha = 0.05$. As k rises from 1 through 4 to 10, the power falls at a given sample size, the impact being most marked at moderate powers (i.e. 40% to 60%). Similarly, Figure 16.2b reports the impact of changing δ when $k = 1$, at the same α; and Figure 16.2c completes the sequence with an illustration of the consequences of reducing the test significance level from 0.05 through 0.01 to 0.001. Finally, Figure 16.2d compares the two types of test, a $\chi^2(40, T\delta)$ (with fixed degrees of freedom as in a coefficient hypothesis test) and a $\chi^2(T, T\delta)$ (which would be a forecast sample constancy test). Naturally, they produce equal results at $T = 40$, but for larger (smaller) sample sizes the former (latter) is more powerful. The figure also shows the comparative effects of increasing the non-centrality parameter on both types of test; the power functions are closer for all sample sizes at the larger non-centrality.

References

Aldrich, J. (1989). Autonomy, *Oxford Economic Papers*, **41**, 15–34.

Baillie, R. T. (1979). Asymptotic prediction mean squared error for vector autoregressive models, *Biometrika*, **66**, 675–678.

Banerjee, A., Dolado, J. J., Galbraith, J. W. and Hendry, D. F. (1993). *Co-integration, Error Correction and the Econometric Analysis of Non-Stationary Data*. Oxford: Oxford University Press.

Boswijk, H. P. and Doornik, J. A. (1999). Distribution approximations for cointegration tests with stationary exogenous regressors, www.nuff.ox.ac.uk/users/doornik, Nuffield College.

Breusch, T. S. (1978). Testing for autocorrelation in dynamic linear models, *Australian Economic Papers*, **17**, 334–355.

Breusch, T. S. and Pagan, A. R. (1980). The Lagrange multiplier test and its applications to model specification in econometrics, *Review of Economic Studies*, **47**, 239–253.

Brown, R. L., Durbin, J. and Evans, J. M. (1975). Techniques for testing the constancy of regression relationships over time (with discussion), *Journal of the Royal Statistical Society B*, **37**, 149–192.

Campos, J. (1986). Finite-sample properties of the instrumental-variables estimator for dynamic simultaneous-equation subsystems with ARMA disturbances, *Journal of Econometrics*, **3**, 333–366.

Campos, J., Ericsson, N. R. and Hendry, D. F. (1996). Cointegration tests in the presence of structural breaks, *Journal of Econometrics*, **70**, 187–220.

Chow, G. C. (1960). Tests of equality between sets of coefficients in two linear regressions, *Econometrica*, **28**, 591–605.

Clements, M. P. and Hendry, D. F. (1999). *Forecasting Non-stationary Economic Time Series*. Cambridge, Mass.: MIT Press.

Cochran, W. G. and Cox, G. M. (1957). *Experimental Designs*. New York: John Wiley.

Conlisk, J. (1974). Optimal response surface designs in Monte Carlo sampling experiments, *Annals of Economic and Social Measurement*, **3**, 463–473.

Cox, D. R. (1958). *Planning of Experiments*. New York: John Wiley and Sons.

Cox, D. R. (1970). *The Analysis of Binary Data*. London: Chapman and Hall.

Dagpunar, J. (1988). *Principles of Random Variate Generation*. Oxford: Oxford University Press.

Davidson, J. E. H., Hendry, D. F., Srba, F. and Yeo, J. S. (1978). Econometric modelling of the aggregate time-series relationship between consumers' expenditure and income in the United Kingdom, *Economic Journal*, **88**, 661–692. Reprinted in Hendry, D. F., *Econometrics: Alchemy or Science?* Oxford: Blackwell Publishers, 1993, and Oxford University Press, 2000.

Davidson, R. and MacKinnon, J. G. (1990). Regression-based methods for using control and antithetic variates in Monte Carlo experiments, Mimeo, Economics Department, Queen's University, Canada.

Davidson, R. and MacKinnon, J. G. (1993). *Estimation and Inference in Econometrics*. Oxford: Oxford University Press.

Devroye, L. (1986). *Non-Uniform Random Variate Generation*. New York: Springer-Verlag.

Dickey, D. A. and Fuller, W. A. (1979). Distribution of the estimators for autoregressive time series with a unit root, *Journal of the American Statistical Association*, **74**, 427–431.

Dickey, D. A. and Fuller, W. A. (1981). Likelihood ratio statistics for autoregressive time series with a unit root, *Econometrica*, **49**, 1057–1072.

Domowitz, I. and White, H. (1982). Mis-specified models with dependent observations, *Journal of Econometrics*, **20**, 35–58.

Doornik, J. A. (1995). *Econometric Computing*. Oxford: University of Oxford. Ph.D Thesis.

Doornik, J. A. (1996). Testing vector autocorrelation and heteroscedasticity in dynamic models, www.nuff.ox.ac.uk/users/doornik, Nuffield College.

Doornik, J. A. (1998). Approximations to the asymptotic distribution of cointegration tests, *Journal of Economic Surveys*, **12**, 573–593. Reprinted in M. McAleer and L. Oxley (1999). *Practical Issues in Cointegration Analysis*. Oxford: Blackwell Publishers.

Doornik, J. A. (2001). *Object-Oriented Matrix Programming using Ox* 4th edition. London: Timberlake Consultants Press.

Doornik, J. A. and Hansen, H. (1994). An omnibus test for univariate and multivariate normality, Discussion paper, Nuffield College.

Doornik, J. A. and Hendry, D. F. (2001a). *GiveWin: An Interface to Empirical Modelling* 3rd edition. London: Timberlake Consultants Press.

Doornik, J. A. and Hendry, D. F. (2001b). *Modelling Dynamic Systems using PcGive: Volume II* 2nd edition. London: Timberlake Consultants Press.

Doornik, J. A., Hendry, D. F. and Nielsen, B. (1998). Inference in cointegrated models: UK M1 revisited, *Journal of Economic Surveys*, **12**, 533–572. Reprinted in M. McAleer and L. Oxley (1999). *Practical Issues in Cointegration Analysis*. Oxford: Blackwell Publishers.

Engle, R. F. and Granger, C. W. J. (1987). Cointegration and error correction: Representation, estimation and testing, *Econometrica*, **55**, 251–276.

Engle, R. F. and Hendry, D. F. (1993). Testing super exogeneity and invariance in regression models, *Journal of Econometrics*, **56**, 119–139. Reprinted in Ericsson, N. R. and Irons, J. S. (eds.) *Testing Exogeneity*, Oxford: Oxford University Press, 1994.

Engle, R. F., Hendry, D. F. and Richard, J.-F. (1983). Exogeneity, *Econometrica*, **51**, 277–304. Reprinted in Hendry, D. F., *Econometrics: Alchemy or Science?* Oxford: Blackwell Publishers, 1993, and Oxford University Press, 2000; and in Ericsson, N. R. and Irons, J. S. (eds.) *Testing Exogeneity*, Oxford: Oxford University Press, 1994.

Ericsson, N. R. (1986). Post-simulation analysis of Monte Carlo experiments: Interpreting Pesaran's (1974) study of non-nested hypothesis test statistics, *Review of Economic Studies*, **53**, 691–707.

Ericsson, N. R. (1991). Monte Carlo methodology and the finite sample properties of instrumental variables statistics for testing nested and non-nested hypotheses, *Econometrica*, **59**, 1249–1277.

Ericsson, N. R. and Irons, J. S. (1995). The Lucas critique in practice: Theory without measurement, In Hoover, K. D. (ed.), *Macroeconometrics: Developments, Tensions and Prospects.* Dordrecht: Kluwer Academic Press.

Ericsson, N. R. and MacKinnon, J. G. (1999). Distributions of error correction tests for cointegration, International finance discussion paper no. 655, Federal Reserve Board of Governors, Washington, D.C. www.bog.frb.fed.us/pubs/ifdp/1999/655/default.htm.

Ericsson, N. R. and Marquez, J. R. (1989). Exact and approximate multi-period mean-square forecast errors for dynamic econometric models, International finance discussion paper 348, Federal Reserve Board.

Ericsson, N. R. and Marquez, J. R. (1998). A framework for economic forecasting, *Econometric Journal*, **1**, C228–C266.

Favero, C. and Hendry, D. F. (1992). Testing the Lucas critique: A review, *Econometric Reviews*, **11**, 265–306.

Frisch, R. (1938). Statistical versus theoretical relations in economic macrodynamics, Mimeograph dated 17 July 1938, League of Nations Memorandum. Reproduced by University of Oslo in 1948 with Tinbergen's comments. Contained in Memorandum 'Autonomy of Economic Relations', 6 November 1948, Oslo, Universitets Økonomiske Institutt. Reprinted in Hendry D. F. and Morgan M. S. (1995), *The Foundations of Econometric Analysis.* Cambridge: Cambridge University Press.

Gentle, J. E. (1998). *Random Number Generation and Monte Carlo Methods.* New York: Springer Verlag.

Godfrey, L. G. (1978). Testing for higher order serial correlation in regression equations when the regressors include lagged dependent variables, *Econometrica*, **46**, 1303–1313.

Gonzalo, J. (1989). Comparison of five alternative methods of estimating long run equilibrium relationships, Discussion paper 89–55, University of California at San Diego.

Govaerts, B., Hendry, D. F. and Richard, J.-F. (1994). Encompassing in stationary linear dynamic models, *Journal of Econometrics*, **63**, 245–270.

Granger, C. W. J. (1969). Investigating causal relations by econometric models and cross-spectral methods, *Econometrica*, **37**, 424–438.

Griliches, Z. and Intriligator, M. D. (eds.)(1984). *Handbook of Econometrics*, Vol. 2–3. Amsterdam: North-Holland.

Haavelmo, T. (1944). The probability approach in econometrics, *Econometrica*, **12**, 1–118. Supplement.

Hammersley, J. M. and Handscomb, D. C. (1964). *Monte Carlo Methods.* London: Chapman and Hall.

Hendry, D. F. (1973). On asymptotic theory and finite sample experiments, *Economica*, **40**, 210–217.

Hendry, D. F. (1974). Stochastic specification in an aggregate demand model of the United Kingdom, *Econometrica*, **42**, 559–578. Reprinted in Hendry, D. F., *Econometrics: Alchemy or Science?* Oxford: Blackwell Publishers, 1993, and Oxford University Press, 2000.

Hendry, D. F. (1975). The consequences of mis-specification of dynamic structure, autocorrelation and simultaneity in a simple model with an application to the demand for imports, In Renton, G. A. (ed.), *Modelling the Economy*, Ch. 11. London: Heinemann Educational Books.

Hendry, D. F. (1979a). The behaviour of inconsistent instrumental variables estimators in dynamic systems with autocorrelated errors, *Journal of Econometrics*, **9**, 295–314.

Hendry, D. F. (1979b). Predictive failure and econometric modelling in macro-economics: The transactions demand for money, In Ormerod, P. (ed.), *Economic Modelling*, pp. 217–242. London: Heinemann. Reprinted in Hendry, D. F., *Econometrics: Alchemy or Science?* Oxford: Blackwell Publishers, 1993, and Oxford University Press, 2000.

Hendry, D. F. (1982). A reply to Professors Maasoumi and Phillips, *Journal of Econometrics*, **19**, 203–213.

Hendry, D. F. (1984). Monte Carlo experimentation in econometrics, in Griliches and Intriligator (1984), Ch. 16.

Hendry, D. F. (1988). The encompassing implications of feedback versus feedforward mechanisms in econometrics, *Oxford Economic Papers*, **40**, 132–149. Reprinted in Ericsson, N. R. and Irons, J. S. (eds.) *Testing Exogeneity*, Oxford: Oxford University Press, 1994.

Hendry, D. F. (1990). Using PC-NAIVE in teaching econometrics, *Oxford Bulletin of Economics and Statistics*, **53**, 199–223.

Hendry, D. F. (1995a). *Dynamic Econometrics*. Oxford: Oxford University Press.

Hendry, D. F. (1995b). *Dynamic Econometrics*. Oxford: Oxford University Press.

Hendry, D. F. (1995c). On the interactions of unit roots and exogeneity, *Econometric Reviews*, **14**, 383–419.

Hendry, D. F. (1997). The econometrics of macro-economic forecasting, *Economic Journal*, **107**, 1330–1357. Reprinted in T.C. Mills (ed.), Economic Forecasting. Edward Elgar, 1999.

Hendry, D. F. (2000). On detectable and non-detectable structural change, *Structural Change and Economic Dynamics*, **11**, 45–65.

Hendry, D. F. and Doornik, J. A. (1997). The implications for econometric modelling of forecast failure, *Scottish Journal of Political Economy*, **44**, 437–461. Special Issue.

Hendry, D. F. and Doornik, J. A. (2001). *Empirical Econometric Modelling using PcGive: Volume I* 3rd edition. London: Timberlake Consultants Press.

Hendry, D. F. and Harrison, R. W. (1974). Monte Carlo methodology and the small sample behaviour of ordinary and two-stage least squares, *Journal of Econometrics*, **2**, 151–174.

Hendry, D. F. and Mizon, G. E. (1978). Serial correlation as a convenient simplification, not a nuisance: A comment on a study of the demand for money by the Bank of England, *Economic Journal*, **88**, 549–563. Reprinted in Hendry, D. F., *Econometrics: Alchemy or Science?* Oxford: Blackwell Publishers, 1993, and Oxford University Press, 2000.

Hendry, D. F. and Mizon, G. E. (2000). Reformulating empirical macro-econometric modelling, *Oxford Review of Economic Policy*, **16**, 138–159.

Hendry, D. F. and Morgan, M. S. (1995). *The Foundations of Econometric Analysis*. Cambridge: Cambridge University Press.

Hendry, D. F. and Neale, A. J. (1987). Monte Carlo experimentation using PC-NAIVE, In Fomby, T. and Rhodes, G. F. (eds.), *Advances in Econometrics*, Vol. 6, pp. 91–125. Greenwich, Connecticut: Jai Press Inc.

Hendry, D. F. and Neale, A. J. (1991). A Monte Carlo study of the effects of structural breaks on tests for unit roots, In Hackl, P. and Westlund, A. H. (eds.), *Economic Structural Change, Analysis and Forecasting*, pp. 95–119. Berlin: Springer-Verlag.

Hendry, D. F., Neale, A. J. and Ericsson, N. R. (1991). *PC-NAIVE, An Interactive Program for*

Monte Carlo Experimentation in Econometrics. Version 6.0. Oxford: Institute of Economics and Statistics, University of Oxford.

Hendry, D. F. and Richard, J.-F. (1989). Recent developments in the theory of encompassing, In Cornet, B. and Tulkens, H. (eds.), *Contributions to Operations Research and Economics. The XXth Anniversary of CORE*, pp. 393–440. Cambridge, MA: MIT Press.

Hendry, D. F. and Srba, F. (1980). AUTOREG: A computer program library for dynamic econometric models with autoregressive errors, *Journal of Econometrics*, **12**, 85–102. Reprinted in Hendry, D. F., *Econometrics: Alchemy or Science?* Oxford: Blackwell Publishers, 1993, and Oxford University Press, 2000.

Hendry, D. F. and Trivedi, P. K. (1972). Maximum likelihood estimation of difference equations with moving-average errors: A simulation study, *Review of Economic Studies*, **32**, 117–145.

Hurwicz, L. (1950). Least squares bias in time series, In Koopmans, T. C. (ed.), *Statistical Inference in Dynamic Economic Models*, No. 10 in Cowles Commission Monograph, Ch. 15. New York: John Wiley & Sons.

Johansen, S. (1988). Statistical analysis of cointegration vectors, *Journal of Economic Dynamics and Control*, **12**, 231–254. Reprinted in R.F. Engle and C.W.J. Granger (eds), Long-Run Economic Relationships, Oxford: Oxford University Press, 1991, 131–52.

Johansen, S. (1995). *Likelihood-based Inference in Cointegrated Vector Autoregressive Models.* Oxford: Oxford University Press.

Johnson, N. L., Kotz, S. and Balakrishnan, N. (1994). *Continuous Univariate Distributions – 1* 2nd edition. New York: John Wiley.

Johnson, N. L., Kotz, S. and Balakrishnan, N. (1995). *Continuous Univariate Distributions – 2* 2nd edition. New York: John Wiley.

Kennedy, W. J. J. and Gentle, J. E. (1980). *Statistical Computing.* New York: Marcel Dekker Inc.

Kiviet, J. F. (1986). On the rigor of some mis-specification tests for modelling dynamic relationships, *Review of Economic Studies*, **53**, 241–261.

Kiviet, J. F. and Phillips, G. D. A. (1992). Exact similar tests for unit roots and cointegration, *Oxford Bulletin of Economics and Statistics*, **54**, 349–367.

Kleijnen, J. P. C. (1974). *Statistical Techniques in Simulation.* New York: Marcel Dekker Inc.

Klein, L. R. (1974). *A Textbook of Econometrics,* 2nd edition. Englewood Cliffs, New Jersey: Prentice-Hall.

Kremers, J. J. M., Ericsson, N. R. and Dolado, J. J. (1992). The power of cointegration tests, *Oxford Bulletin of Economics and Statistics*, **54**, 325–348.

L'Ecuyer, P. (1997). Tables of maximally-equidistributed combined LSFR generators, Mimeo, University of Montreal, Canada.

Lucas, R. E. (1974). Expectations and the neutrality of money, *Journal of Economic Theory*, **4**, 103–124.

Maasoumi, E. and Phillips, P. C. B. (1982). On the behaviour of inconsistent instrumental variables estimators, *Journal of Econometrics*, **19**, 183–201.

MacKinnon, J. G. (1991). Critical values for cointegration tests, In Engle, R. F. and Granger, C. W. J. (eds.), *Long-Run Economic Relationships*, pp. 267–276. Oxford: Oxford University Press.

Maddala, G. S. (1977). *Econometrics.* New York: McGraw-Hill.

Mann, H. and Wald, A. (1943). On stochastic limit and order relationships, *Annals of Mathematical Statistics*, **14**, 217–226.

Marsaglia, G. and Bray, T. A. (1964). A convenient method for generating random normal variables, *SIAM Review*, **6**, 260–264.

Metropolis, N. and Ulam, S. (1949). The Monte Carlo method, *Journal of the American Statistical Association*, **44**, 335–341.

Mizon, G. E. and Hendry, D. F. (1980). An empirical application and Monte Carlo analysis of tests of dynamic specification, *Review of Economic Studies*, **49**, 21–45. Reprinted in Hendry, D. F., *Econometrics: Alchemy or Science?* Oxford: Blackwell Publishers, 1993, and Oxford University Press, 2000.

Nagar, A. L. (1959). The bias and moment matrix of the general k-class estimators of the parameters in simultaneous equations, *Econometrica*, **27**, 575–595.

Naylor, T. H. (1971). *Computer Simulation Experiments with Models of Economic Systems*. New York: John Wiley.

Nickell, S. J. (1981). An investigation of the determinants of manufacturing employmnet in the United Kingdom, Discussion paper 105, Center for Labour Economics, London School of Economics.

Nielsen, B. (2001). The asymptotic distribution of unit root test of unstable autoregressive processes, *Econometrica*, **69**, 211–219.

Orcutt, G. H. and Cochrane, D. (1949). A sampling study of the merits of autoregressive and reduced form transformations in regression analysis, *Journal of the American Statistical Association*, **44**, 356–372.

Orcutt, G. H. and Winokur, H. S. (1969). First order autoregression: Inference, estimation and prediction, *Econometrica*, **37**, 1–14.

Park, S. and Miller, K. (1988). Random number generators: Good ones are hard to find, *Communications of the ACM*, **31**, 1192–1201.

Perron, P. (1989). The Great Crash, the oil price shock and the unit root hypothesis, *Econometrica*, **57**, 1361–1401.

Pesaran, M. H. (1974). On the general problem of model selection, *Review of Economic Studies*, **41**, 153–171.

Phillips, P. C. B. (1977). A general theorem in the theory of asymptotic expansions as approximations to finite sample distributions of econometric estimators, *Econometrica*, **45**, 1517–1534.

Phillips, P. C. B. (1982). Best uniform and modified Padé approximants to probability densities in econometrics, In Hildenbrand, W. (ed.), *Advances in Econometrics*, pp. 123–167. Cambridge: Cambridge University Press.

Phillips, P. C. B. (1987a). Time series regression with a unit root, *Econometrica*, **55**, 277–301.

Phillips, P. C. B. (1987b). Towards a unified asymptotic theory for autoregression, *Biometrika*, **74**, 535–547.

Phillips, P. C. B. (1988). Regression theory for near-integrated time series, *Econometrica*, **56**, 1021–1043.

Phillips, P. C. B. (1989). Partially identified econometric models, *Econometric Theory*, **5**, 181–240.

Phillips, P. C. B. and Loretan, M. (1991). Estimating long-run economic equilibria, *Review of*

Economic Studies, **58**, 407–436.

Phillips, P. C. B. and Wickens, M. R. (1978). *Exercises in Econometrics*. Oxford: Philip Allan.

Phillips, P. C. B. and Xiao, Z. (1998). A primer on unit root testing, *Journal of Economic Surveys*, **12**, 423–447.

Ripley, B. D. (1987). *Stochastic Simulation*. New York: John Wiley & Sons.

Sargan, J. D. (1980a). A model of wage-price inflation, *Review of Economic Studies*, **47**, 979–1012. Reprinted as pp. 170–190 in Sargan J. D. (1988), *Contributions to Econometrics*, Vol. 1, Cambridge: Cambridge University Press.

Sargan, J. D. (1980b). Some tests of dynamic specification for a single equation, *Econometrica*, **48**, 879–897. Reprinted as pp. 191–212 in Sargan J. D. (1988), *Contributions to Econometrics*, Vol. 1, Cambridge: Cambridge University Press.

Sargan, J. D. (1982). On Monte Carlo estimates of moments that are infinite, In Basmann, R. L. and Rhodes, G. F. (eds.), *Advances in Econometrics: A Research Annual*, Vol. 1, pp. 267–299. Greenwich, Connecticut: Jai Press Inc.

Sargan, J. D. (1988). *Lectures on Advanced Econometric Theory*. Oxford: Basil Blackwell.

Schmidt, P. (1974). The asymptotic distribution of forecasts in the dynamic simulation of an econometric model, *Econometrica*, **42**, 303–309.

Shenton, L. R. and Johnson, W. L. (1965). Moments of a serial correlation coefficient, *Journal of the Royal Statistical Society B*, **27**, 308–320.

Silverman, B. W. (1986). *Density Estimation for Statistics and Data Analysis*. London: Chapman and Hall.

Sobol', I. M. (1974). *The Monte Carlo Method*. Chicago: University of Chicago Press.

Sowey, E. R. (1973). Stochastic simulation of macroeconomic models: Methodology and interpretation, In Powell, A. A. and Williams, R. A. (eds.), *Econometric Studies of Macro and Monetary Relations*, Ch. 8. Amsterdam: North-Holland Publishing Company.

Student (1908). On the probable error of the mean, *Biometrika*, **6**, 1–25.

Summers, R. (1959). A strategy for appraising various simultaneous equation estimating methods by means of sampling experiments, Mimeo, Cowles Foundation, Yale University, New Haven.

Summers, R. (1965). A capital intensive approach to the small sample properties of various simultaneous equation estimators, *Econometrica*, **33**, 1–41.

Teräsvirta, T. (1970). *Stepwise Regression and Economic Forecasting*. No. 31 in Economic Studies Monograph. Helsinki: Finnish Economic Association.

Tocher, K. D. (1963). *The Art of Simulation*. London: English Universities Press.

White, H. (1980a). A heteroskedastic-consistent covariance matrix estimator and a direct test for heteroskedasticity, *Econometrica*, **48**, 817–838.

White, H. (1980b). Non-linear regression on cross-section data, *Econometrica*, **48**, 721–746.

White, H. (1990). A consistent model selection, In Granger, C. W. J. (ed.), *Modelling Economic Series*, pp. 369–383. Oxford: Clarendon Press.

Yule, G. U. (1926). Why do we sometimes get nonsense-correlations between time-series? A study in sampling and the nature of time series (with discussion), *Journal of the Royal Statistical Society*, **89**, 1–64.

Author Index

Subject Index